TECHNOLOGY AND THE HUMAN CONDITION

BERNARD GENDRON

Technology and the Human Condition

ST. MARTIN'S PRESS
New York

FOR SARAH AND TIMOTHY

Cover design: Rick Fiala

Library of Congress Catalog Card Number: 76-28120
Copyright © 1977 by St. Martin's Press, Inc.
All Rights Reserved.
Manufactured in the United States of America.
54321
fed
For information, write: St. Martin's Press, Inc.,
175 Fifth Avenue, New York, N.Y. 10010

CONTENTS

PREFACE

Technology has been given most of the credit for ongoing improvements in the conditions of human life and most of the blame for deterioration in these conditions. Indeed, technology sometimes seems to have replaced God or the devil as the officially recognized benefactor or malefactor of humankind.

The existence of such extreme views is not surprising. After all, technology does insinuate itself into every corner of our lives. It seems to have a dynamism all of its own. And it seems overwhelmingly to shape and transform our lives for better or for worse. No wonder that many attribute divine or demonic powers to it.

Unfortunately, too many views of technology arise out of ignorance or confusion about its workings and merely express unreflected emotional responses to it. This again is not surprising. Despite its omnipresence, technology is still a great mystery to us. We have considerable understanding of the internal mechanisms of various technologies, but little understanding of their social role. The widespread acceptance of views ranging from the most unabashedly *pro*technological to the most adamantly *anti*technological attests to the paucity of our knowledge and the depth of our confusion.

This book analyzes critically some representative views of the social role of technology. In doing so it addresses two fundamental questions: First, what are the nature and extent of technology's impact on social institutions and individual lives? Second, to what degree is this impact beneficial and to what degree harmful?

This book is interdisciplinary, both in the broad sense that it combines the humanistic and scientific perspectives and in the narrow sense that it draws its information from a number of different branches of science. On the one hand, it embodies humanistic standards in evaluating the performance and potential of technology. On the other hand, it employs the theories and data of psychology, sociology, economics, and other branches of science in determining what the performance and the potential are. In this area of study, the humanistic and scientific approaches can hardly proceed independently of each other.

For what is good in this book, my greatest debt is to my students of the past six years, but especially to David Allen and Nancy Folbre. Ian Barbour, Steven Puro, Julius Sensat, and Albert Teich have read an earlier draft of the manuscript in full and have made many valuable suggestions. I have benefited also from suggestions and criticisms by friends and colleagues who read sample chapters of earlier drafts: Edwin Allaire, Carl Hedman, Nancy Holstrom, Hardy Jones, Robert Palter, and Thomas Seung. I am deeply grateful for the enthusiastic encouragement I received at the early stages from Irwin Lieb and Thomas Seung, and in the later stages from Carl Hedman and Ray Merritt.

The painstaking editorial work of the staff at St. Martin's Press has led to significant improvements in the style and tone of the manuscript. I am especially indebted to Anita S. Morse for her valuable suggestions and telling criticisms. Florence Heywood did a fine job of typing an earlier draft of the manuscript. A special word of thanks is due to Valerie Kaiser, who typed the last two drafts, sometimes under severe time constraints: I admire the skill, ingenuity, and care which she brings to her work.

An earlier version of chapter 4 ("The Brave New World Reconsidered") was published in *Philosophy Forum*, 15, No. 1–2 (combined issue). I thank the editor for permission to reprint it with modification.

TECHNOLOGY AND THE
HUMAN CONDITION

1

Introduction

An Overview

The public debate initiated in the 1960s over the social impact of technology has not yet subsided. The issues are overwhelming, and no resolution is in sight. The following questions are primarily being asked: Is technology a progressive social force? Does it on balance contribute to the amelioration of the human condition? Has it led to a significant decrease in human pain, suffering, oppression, and exploitation? Has it really enabled us to enrich our existence, and to expand our powers over our own fate? Or, on the other hand, has it proved on balance to be a regressive force? Has it restricted our life options and frustrated our freedoms? Has it dehumanized us, alienated us, or generally impoverished our daily lives? Has it undermined our relations with each other and with nature? Or, alternatively, is technology "neutral"? Are we and not technology responsible ultimately for the goods or evils which appear to have been visited upon us by our technology? But do we really control technology or does it control us? And, indeed, are its social effects as widespread as they initially appear?

Of course these questions are not new. They have been raised with equal fervor at various times since the emergence of modern science in the sixteenth century, particularly since the onset of the industrial revolution in the eighteenth century. But new facts and developments since World War II have made these questions especially relevant and their resolution more urgent: the atom bomb, the space race, economic growth and the new affluence, accelerated technological innovation, the political rise of technocrats, the computer revolution, growing pollution, the resource crisis, and the so-called "blue-collar blues."

There has been an avalanche of both popular and semipopular literature on the social role of technology, much of it stimulating and some of it insightful. Nonetheless, we are still nowhere near a satisfactory answer to any of the main questions. We are confused about the issues, and have little idea of how to go about resolving them. And we have no theories sufficiently articulated and detailed to be tested. This is not wholly the fault of the literature on technology; the issues are too global and emotion-charged. We simply do not know enough of the relevant psychological and sociological facts, and we disagree too much on the standards for measuring social progress and regress. Yet, given the knowledge at our disposal, we should have advanced much farther than we have in our attempt to answer questions concerning the social role of technology. We should have the issues more in focus, a clearer sense of what is needed to resolve these issues, and a better idea of which general views about the social impact of technology are plausible and which are not. For this failure the literature on technology is partly at fault. It is for the most part too vague, biased, impressionistic, superficial, logically sloppy, and unpersuasive.

I hope in this book to remedy some of these deficiencies. I conceive of it as an introduction to the study and assessment of the social role of modern technology. In it I sift out the major questions and issues, explain the key terms and concepts, and where possible resolve the differences between them.

I begin by summarizing three "extreme" views concerning the social role and value of modern technology: the Utopian view, the Dystopian view, and the Socialist view. I spend the remainder of the book developing these views, setting them into conflict with one another, and then attempting to determine which is closest to the truth. The analysis of the ways in which these views oppose one another provides the unifying framework and sets the tone for a discussion of the major issues and controversies concerning the social role of technology. Within the context of this debate, the key questions, concepts, and distinctions relating to all these issues and controversies, and the appropriate strategies for their investigation, will present themselves naturally and in due course. The resolution of this debate will presuppose that these distinctions and concepts have been adequately analyzed, and that these questions have been answered as well as is possible.

Three Views

According to the Utopian view, all or most of our social progress is due primarily or exclusively to the growth of technology. Indeed, Utopians believe that technological growth, if unimpeded by any major disaster, will in the long run bring about the demise of every major social evil. They believe that it will eliminate scarcity and disease, that it will significantly improve communications and education, and that it will undermine the environmental conditions which reinforce aggression, prejudice, sectarianism, nationalism, oppression, and exploitation. Utopians construe the major world problems as "technical," rather than as "political" or "ideological."

The Dystopian view is the exact opposite of the Utopian view. Dystopians believe that technological growth in the long run generates or intensifies many more social evils than it reduces or eliminates. According to them, while technology is creating affluence and increasing our collective power over nature it is undermining freedom and democracy; it is stimulating the growth of bureaucracy and the use of techniques of mass manipulation; it is cutting humans off from nature, their bodies, and their fellow humans; it is making work more tedious, unchallenging, and psychologically unhealthy; and it is increasing the dangers of annihilatory war and ecological catastrophe.

Socialists agree with the Utopians that technological growth is a necessary condition for social progress, and that, in the proper circumstances, technology can be used successfully to alleviate or eliminate most of the major social ills. But Socialists insist that technological growth is far from a sufficient condition for overall social progress. They agree with the Dystopians that technology can have disastrous effects; and they are quick to point out the alienating, dehumanizing, and ecologically disruptive consequences of technology in capitalist societies. However, in opposition both to the Utopians and Dystopians, Socialists insist that technological growth in the social context is neither automatically progressive nor regressive. According to them, this depends on the kind of economic system within which technological growth takes place and on the economic classes which control its use. Thus, within mature capitalism, and when controlled by capitalist classes, it is on balance socially harmful; within socialist societies, and when controlled by the working class, it is on balance socially beneficial. According to Socialists, social progress is dependent on economic and political revolutions which are partially independent of technological revolutions. If these political and economic revolutions do not take place, then all the scientific and technological development in the world will fail to stimulate even a modicum of social progress.

The Literature

There has been an abundance of Utopian literature since World War II. It varies considerably in scope, depth, rigor, perspective, and attitude. No one book is complete and representative; a coherent Utopian view can only be constructed out of many bits and pieces taken from a variety of Utopian books.

B. F. Skinner, Buckminster Fuller, C. P. Snow, Marshall McLuhan, Alvin Toffler, John Maynard Keynes, and John Kenneth Galbraith are the better known Utopian writers.[1] Behind them stands a host of more obscure but no less enthusiastic proponents, such as Gerald Feinberg, Zbigniew Brzezinski, Herman Kahn, Arthur Clarke, Robert Blauner, and Robert Theobald.[2] Altogether they are a very mixed crew. Their points of view represent a variety of disciplines: physics (Snow), psychology (Skinner), political science (Brzezinski), sociology (Bell), economics (Keynes and Galbraith), communications (McLuhan), architecture (Fuller). Some are euphorically optimistic (Skinner and Clarke), while others are only qualifiedly optimistic (Bell and Galbraith). Some deal speculatively with the distant future (Clarke and Kahn), while others delve cautiously only into the more immediate future (Snow and Bell).

These writers also differ on what they take to be the most important emancipatory consequences of modern technology. Some focus primarily on the elimination of scarcity (Keynes, Clarke and Fuller), while others focus on the growth of leisure (Theobald), the emergence of a sensate culture (Toffler), the rise of a meritocracy (Bell and Galbraith), the development of a global community (McLuhan), the demise of ideology (Bell), the new techniques of behavior control (Skinner), the rising power of scientists and technicians (Bell), the elimination of labor alienation (Blauner), or even the emergence of a race of superhumans and the elimination of death (Clarke and Feinberg).

The Dystopians are also a fairly mixed group, including, in the past, men of letters, humanities teachers, and clerics, and, more recently, literary representatives of the "hip" or counterculture. Belonging to the first category are Fedor Dostoevski (*Notes from the Underground*), Oswald Spengler (*Decline of the West*), Petrim Sorokin (*The Crisis of our Age*), Aldous Huxley (*Brave New World*), George Orwell (*1984*), and Jacques Ellul (*Technological Society*).[3] To the latter category belong Herbert Marcuse (*One Dimensional Man*), Theodore Roszak (*The Making of a Counter-Culture*), Charles Reich (*The Greening of America*), and Philip Slater (*The Pursuit of Loneliness*).[4]

There is little Socialist literature dealing thematically and systematically with the social role of technology, and what there is comes mainly from the Marxist tradition. From Karl Marx's *Capital* and from Friedrich Engels's *Socialism: Utopian or Scientific*, we can reconstruct a Socialist view of the social role of technology within capitalism, and from V. I. Lenin's *State* and *Revolution* (and perhaps Mao Tse-tung's philosophical essays), we can reconstruct a Socialist view of the social role of technology within socialism and communism.[5]

An Outline of the Book

Part one presents a fairly plausible version of the Utopian view, and analyzes its responses to the more obvious objections. Part two summarizes the various Dystopian criticisms of technology and attempts to determine the extent to which they are successful, especially in light of possible Utopian and Socialist rejoinders. Part three outlines the Socialist view of the relation between technology and society, and critically examines the differences between Socialists and their Utopian and Dystopian antagonists. I conclude that the Socialist criticisms of the Utopian and Dystopian views are powerful and generally successful.

Socialists can counter the Utopian and Dystopian criticisms more effectively than Utopians and Dystopians can counter criticisms coming from the Socialists. However this does not mean the Socialist view is the true view of the social role of technology, but rather that the Socialist view is at present preferable to the other two I have discussed. A new view synthesizing the best elements of these three might well emerge in the future, but at present no such view is in the offing. Though effective as a tool for criticism, the Socialist view is still too underdeveloped in its positive claims about technology and society to be tested conclusively; Socialists have not sufficiently developed a theory of the dynamic role of technology in history, or even of the role of technology within socialist and communist societies. Indeed, significantly more investigative work must be done before some general view of the social role of technology can merit final acceptance. Nonetheless, though in this study no definitive theory of the social role of technology is formulated and fully defended, the discussion of the different theories does provide a fairly complete introduction to the social study of technology, and does draw from the evidence whatever conclusions can be drawn. This may not be all that one would like, but it is progress enough.

Notes

[1]B. F. Skinner, *Walden Two* (New York: Macmillan, 1948), and *Beyond Freedom and Dignity* (New York: Knopf, 1971); R. Buckminster Fuller, *Utopia or Oblivion* (New York: Bantam, 1969); C. P. Snow, *The Two Cultures* and *A Second Look* (London: Cambridge, 1964); Marshall McLuhan, *Understanding Media* (New York: McGraw Hill, 1964); Alvin Toffler, *Future Shock* (New York: Bantam, 1970); Daniel Bell, *The Coming of Post-Industrial Society* (New York: Basic Books, 1973); John Maynard Keynes, "Economic Possibilities for our Grandchildren," in *Essays in Persuasion* (London: Macmillan, 1972); John Kenneth Galbraith, *The Affluent Society* (New York: New American Library, 1972).

[2]Gerald Feinberg, *The Prometheus Project* (Garden City: Doubleday, 1969); Zbigniew Brzezinski, *Between Two Ages: America's Role in the Technetronic Era* (New York: Viking, 1970); Herman Kahn and Anthony J. Wiener, *Year Two Thousand* (New York: Macmillan, 1967); Arthur Clarke, *Profiles of the Future* (New York: Bantam, 1964); Robert Theobald, *The Economics of Abundance* (New York: Pitman, 1970).

[3]Fedor Dostoevski, *Notes from the Underground* (New York: Bantam, 1974); Oswald Spengler, *Decline of the West* (New York: Knopf, 1932); Aldous Huxley, *Brave New World* (New York: Harper & Row, 1969); George Orwell, *1984* (New York: Harcourt,

Brace, 1949); Petrim Sorokin, *Crisis of Our Age* (New York: Dutton, 1941); Jacques Ellul, *Technological Society* (New York: Vintage, 1964).

[4]Herbert Marcuse, *One Dimensional Man* (Boston: Beacon, 1964); Theodore Roszak, *The Making of a Counter-Culture* (Garden City: Doubleday, 1969); Charles Reich, *The Greening of America* (New York: Random House, 1970); Philip Slater, *The Pursuit of Loneliness* (Boston: Beacon, 1970).

[5]Karl Marx, *Capital*, Vol. I (New York: International, 1967); Karl Marx and Friedrich Engels, *Selected Works* (New York: International, 1968); V. I. Lenin, *Selected Works* (New York: International, 1971); Mao Tse-tung, *Four Essays on Philosophy* (Peking: For. Lang. Press, 1968).

Part One

THE UTOPIAN VIEW

2

The Basic Argument

Today it is not terribly fashionable to be a Utopian. Our technology seems helpless in the face of a growing scarcity of food and power, and of economic stagnation and inflation. But not too long ago, technological Utopianism was quite popular. It even received the official blessing of the Kennedy administration and such of its ideologues as John Kennedy himself, John Kenneth Galbraith, Robert McNamara, and Walt Rostow. In a famous speech, Kennedy stressed that "what is at stake in our economic decisions today is not some grand warfare of rival ideologies," but rather the "practical management of a modern economy." What is most needed, he said, is "basic discussion of the *sophisticated and technical* questions involved in keeping a great economic machinery moving ahead," rather than diatribes about political philosophies and ethical principles. While the problems of the 1930s had required "political answers," the problems of the 1960s, he said, primarily required "technical answers."[1] For Kennedy and many of his contemporaries, modern technology was the key to the solution of social problems. In 1968, C. West Churchman, an influential advocate of "systems technologies," asserted that, "We have the technological capacity of adequately feeding, sheltering, and clothing every inhabitant of the world," and "of providing adequate medical care" and "sufficient education" for these same people. In addition, he said, "We have the technological capability of outlawing warfare," of maximizing "freedom of opinion and freedom of action," and of "organizing the societies of the world" to discover and implement these solutions.[2]

And it did seem, in the early 1960s, that technology was doing its job well. Production and affluence seemed indefinitely on the upswing, and class antagonisms on the downswing. The revolution in communications and electronics seemed to be ushering in an age of unprecedented literacy, leisure, and mobility. New drugs promised instant therapy and unlimited mind expansion. But then came the Vietnam War, the "population bomb," and the "energy crisis," and all these anticipations came crashing down. By the early 1970s, the pendulum had swung from Utopianism to Dystopianism. The Ehrlichs, the Elluls, and the Roszaks replaced the Fullers, the McNamaras, and the Skinners as the currently popular gurus.

Nonetheless, with changes in our economic and political horizons as yet unforeseen, the Utopian viewpoint may again gain widespread acceptance. It has experienced fluctuations of this sort before. The Utopian view was in low regard at the onset of the industrial revolution and during the years immediately following World War I, but it bounced back as the fruits of industrialization began to accumulate and the damages of two world wars began to subside.

If only because of its recuperative powers, the Utopian view deserves our critical attention. But, even if it turns out to be blatantly and unqualifiedly false, and its proponents to be philistines of the worst sort, we can still gain much understanding of the social role of technology by finding out why the Utopian view is false and why it attracts the sorts of supporters it does attract.

The Best Utopian Argument

What evidence do Utopians have for claiming that technological growth will in the long run bring about the virtual elimination of every major social evil? This is a highly ambitious and speculative claim—not the kind of carefully hedged and narrowly circumscribed claim one usually encounters in social science books. To justify (or refute) it with scientific certainty would require much more factual data than is presently available. Thus, all we can fairly ask of Utopians is that they make at least a persuasive (if not a conclusive) case for their claim by weaving together in one continuous argument all the diverse data that are available.

Have Utopians been successful in presenting us with such a persuasive argument? It is difficult to answer this question. For one thing, the Utopians have not put up any kind of united argumentative front. They constitute not one but many schools of thought; a variety of arguments for Utopianism have been put forth by a variety of Utopians. Another problem is that Utopians tend to write in a highly popular and informal way; they tend to tell anecdotes and to make dramatic pronouncements rather than to formulate rigorous proofs. Thus, they tend merely to intimate, rather than to state clearly, which arguments they are willing to put forth, and even that they do only fragmentarily and discontinuously.

It would be tedious and insufficiently rewarding to examine every bit of Utopian literature for evidence or arguments, or to survey all the reasons Utopians seem to have for being Utopians. Instead, I will present and examine in some detail what I take to be the best argument for the Utopian view. This argument would not be accepted or emphasized by all Utopians, and no Utopian has expressed it in quite the way that I do here. Nonetheless, this argument, or something very much like it, seems to be presupposed in the work of the more economically oriented Utopians, such as Buckminster Fuller, John Maynard Keynes, Arthur Clarke, and to a lesser extent, C. P. Snow, Alvin Toffler, and Herman Kahn. It is the argument, I think, that Utopians should accept as making the most plausible and interesting case for their view. This argument can be formulated as follows:

Premise 1: We are presently undergoing a postindustrial revolution in technology
Premise 2: In the postindustrial age, technological growth will be sustained
Premise 3: In the postindustrial age, continued technological growth will lead to the elimination of economic scarcity
Premise 4: The elimination of economic scarcity will lead to the elimination of every major social evil

From now on, I shall refer to this argument simply as "the Utopian argument." And I shall spend the remainder of part one examining in some detail the assumptions underlying each of the premises of the argument. But first let me briefly explicate what the argument is.

Scarcity: The Central Problem

There are a host of social evils: poverty, exploitation, imperialism, oppression, crime, war, disease, compulsive consumption, pollution, and alienation. Presumably, some or all are interconnected; some are primary and others secondary; some kinds of evils cause other kinds, and their elimination is a precondition for the elimination of the others. But which evils are primary and which secondary? The Utopian argument states that the primary social evils are economic evils, and indeed that all our major social problems are consequences of our economic problems. Specifically, it says that the most basic social evil is economic scarcity. Economic scarcity exists when there are not enough available economic goods and services to satisfy everyone's more important wants. Needless to say, human societies have always suffered economic scarcity.

In effect, the Utopian argument tells us that we can solve all our major social problems if we are able to solve our economic problems. Specifically, it tells us that we will probably eliminate war, crime, oppression, and the like once we succeed in eliminating economic scarcity. In the final analysis, Utopians ask: Don't all crime, war, and oppression stem from the fact that people are struggling for scarce goods, and that they are frustrated and abused by institutions whose function is to produce, allocate, or administer these scarce goods? If people had all that was necessary to satisfy their important wants, why would anybody resort to crime or war or oppression? With the ending of scarcity, the basis for all other social evils would be undermined.

For example, Arthur Clarke tells us that, paradoxically, societies with superabundant goods and services would commit themselves to spiritualist rather than materialist values. Such societies

> will be so completely different from ours that the present debate between capitalism and communism would become quite meaningless. All material possessions would be literally as cheap as dirt. . . . When material objects are all intrinsically worthless, perhaps only then will a real sense of value arise. Works of art would be cherished because they were beautiful, not because they were rare. Nothing—no "things"—would be as priceless as craftsmanship, personal skills, professional services . . . So we may hope, therefore, that one day our age of roaring factories and bulging warehouses will pass away, as the spinning wheel

and the home loom and the butter churn passed before them. And then our descendants, no longer cluttered up with possessions, will remember what many of us have forgotten—that the only things in the world that really matter are such imponderables as beauty and wisdom, laughter and love.[3]

In the same vein, John Maynard Keynes maintains that once scarcity is eliminated, greed, niggardliness, ambition, and exploitation will lose their useful social functions, and will gradually disappear. He states,

> When the accumulation of wealth is no longer of high social importance, there will be a great change in the code of morals. We shall be able to rid ourselves of many of the pseudo-moral principles which have hag-ridden us for two hundred years, by which we have exalted some of the most distasteful of human qualities into the position of highest virtues . . . The love of money as a possession—as distinguished from the love of money as a means to the enjoyments and realities of life—will be recognized for what it is, a somewhat disgusting morbidity, one of those semi-criminal, semi-psychological propensities which one hands over with a shudder to the specialists in mental disease.[4]

Once the economic problem is solved, he says,

> I see us free, therefore, to return to some of the most sure and certain principles of religion and traditional virtue—that avarice is vice, that the exaction of usury is a misdemeanor, and the love of money is detestable, that those walk most truly in the paths of virtue and sane wisdom who take least thought for the morrow. We shall once more value ends above means and prefer the good to the useful. We shall honor those who can teach us how to pluck the hour and the day virtuously and well, the delightful people who are capable of taking direct enjoyment in things, the lilies of the field who toil not, neither do they spin.[5]

Buckminster Fuller predicts that the elimination of economic scarcity will lead to the elimination of war and other undersirable forms of human aggression:

> As 100 percent of humanity achieves, or nears, physical-survival success, past history's seemingly inexorable reason for war (not enough for both of us) will have been eliminated. . . . Where there is abundance, competition is unnecessary and unthought of . . . Though wars are precipitated by and identified by irrelevant and superficial preoccupying "causes" which are popularly sloganizable, wars have always occurred because of

the underlying inadequacy of vital supplies. We will always have war until there is enough to support all humanity.[6]

Utopians of the past failed, he says, because they did not have the wherewithal to solve the economic problem. They thus directed their efforts at reforming man directly, rather than changing his environment.

The would-be Utopians therefore attempted only metaphysical and ideological transformations of man's nature—unwitting and possible alternatives. It was then unthinkable that there might soon develop a full capacity to satisfactorily transform the physical energy events and the material structure of the environment—not by altering man, but by helping him to become literate and to use his innate cerebral capacities, and thereby at least to achieve man's physical survival at a Utopianly successful level.[7]

Fuller summarizes the case for the primacy of economics in the solution of social problems thusly:

The present top-priority world problem to be solved may be summarized as how to triple, swiftly, safely, and satisfyingly, the overall performance per kilos, kilowatts, and man-hours of the world's comprehensively invested resources of elements, energy, time, and intelligence. To do so will render these resources . . . capable of supporting 100 percent of humanity's increasing population at higher standards of living than any human minority or single individual has ever known or dreamed of and will thus eliminate the cause of war and its weapons' frustrating diversion of productivity from the support of all mankind.[8]

The Eliminability of Scarcity

The Utopians quoted above all agree that *if scarcity is eliminated, then the major social problems will be resolved.* Supposing this is true, then the next question is: will scarcity be eliminated? They answer confidently in the affirmative. Writing in 1930, at the height of the Great Depression, Keynes boldly announced:

I draw the conclusion that, assuming no important wars and no important increases in population, the *economic problem* may be solved, or at least within the sight of a solution, within a hundred years. This means that the economic problem is not—if we look into the future—*the permanent problem of the human race.*[9]

Fuller is even less hesitant about this outcome:

> It is physically practical this minute for the first time in history for men to set themselves methodically to the task of unlimited production for all without invoking a further day of fundamental negative reckoning.[10]

He predicts that the task "of providing enough for all of humanity" will be completed by the year 2000. Clearly, according to him, technology is the cause of decreasing scarcity. Technological growth necessarily entails proportionate increases in total wealth.

> Experimentally demonstrated, wealth is: energy compounded with intellect's knowhow. Science's Law of Conservation of Energy states that "energy cannot be created or destroyed." The first constituent of wealth—energy—is therefore irreducible. . . . Every time man uses the second constituent of wealth—his know-how—this intellectual resource automatically increases. Energy cannot decrease. Know-how can only increase. It is therefore scientifically clear that wealth which combines energy and intellect can only increase, and that wealth can only increase with use and that wealth increases as fast as it is used.[11]

This practical know-how is technology. Thus, technology inevitably grows, and as technology grows so does wealth.

Arthur Clarke envisions that by the year 2100 mankind will have invented the "replicator," that is, a mechanism which can make any thing out of anything, by breaking down the original item (for instance, a handkerchief) into its ultimate constituents and reconstructing a new item out of these constituents (for instance, a diamond). The invention of the replicator would guarantee abundance for everyone.

> The advent of the replicator would mean the end of all factories, and perhaps all transportation of raw materials and all farming. . . . Every family would produce all that it needed on the spot. . . . No one who has read thus far will, I hope, argue that the replicator would be so expensive that nobody could possibly afford it. The prototype, it is true, is hardly likely to cost less than $1 trillion, spread over a few centuries of time. The second model would cost nothing, because the replicator's first job would be to produce other replicators.[12]

Everyone would have their own replicator to produce exactly what they want. Alvin Toffler has predicted that the major problem for future consumers will be "overchoice," rather than inadequate choice, in the purchase of goods and services. Herman Kahn, a professional futurist, has projected for the United States in the year 2020 a per capita gross national product of approximately $30,000 (compared to about $5,000 in 1965); for the world, he has projected a $20,000 per capita income within two hundred years.[13]

The New Technology

Non-Utopians have good reason to resist accepting the assertion that technological growth brings about proportionate decreases in economic scarcity. On this issue, the record of past technology has not been so good. Consider, for example, the case of industrial technology, that is, the technology operative in the industrial revolution and its aftermath (the steam engine, power looms, the Bessemer process in steel production), as well as any technology characteristic of industrial societies (assembly line production, atomic power, the automobile). There is little doubt that the sustained growth of industrial technology has added much to our wealth, and hence contributed to the reduction of certain forms of economic scarcity. But industrial technology has been associated with or contributory to dramatic increases in other forms of scarcity. The number of poor has increased, and our stock of free goods, such as clean air and water, has been seriously depleted. Equally important, our wants and needs have grown as production has grown. (Scarcity, of course, is a function not only of the number of goods and services we produce, but also of the amount of wants and needs we have. Everything else being equal, the more we want, the less satisfied we are, and the more scarcity we experience.) So the record of industrial technology, though in some ways impressive, is far from adequate. It is questionable whether industrial technology by itself can lead us into postscarcity.

Many Utopians concede this, as they must. To this objection, they respond that the industrial age in technology is coming to an end. They tell us that we are undergoing a major new revolution in technology, as momentous or impactful as the industrial revolution. It is called, alternatively, the "second industrial revolution" (Norbert Wiener) or the "postindustrial revolution" (Daniel Bell). It is also identified as the revolution in technology which will usher in a "technetronic era" (Zbigniew Brzezinski), the "postcivilization era" (Kenneth Boulding), or the "superindustrial era" (Alvin Toffler).[14] I shall simply refer to this revolution as the "postindustrial revolution." The distinguishing marks of this postindustrial revolution are the emergence of computer technology, rapid development in electronics, communications, and behavior control, and the widespread use of "intellectual" or "software" technologies, such as operations research, linear programming, and systems design.

According to many Utopians, the postindustrial revolution in technology is bringing about dramatic changes in socioeconomic institutions—the sorts of changes which will enable these institutions to grapple more effectively with the problem of scarcity. First, they argue, the power structure is being transformed; scientists and technicians are replacing politicians and the corporate rich as the chief decision makers of society. Second, the new decision makers will make use of the powerful new intellectual tools for analyzing complex social phenomena and for guiding difficult social choices regarding these phenomena. Many Utopians believe that, with the help of decision theory, game theory, and systems analysis, scientific and technical leaders will be able to pursue long-term social planning with maximum efficiency and rationality. This being the case, society will be able to tackle efficiently the problem of scarcity. By giving rise to a new power structure with its powerful decision-making technology, postindustrial technology, according to Utopians, is paving the way for the resolution of all major social problems. It is able to achieve what industrial technology could never achieve—the generation of the necessary conditions for the elimination of scarcity.[15]

Thus, the viability of the Utopian view depends crucially on the occurrence and nature of the so-called postindustrial revolution in technology. Where is this revolution taking place? The usual answer is that it is occurring primarily in the United States, and less so in certain advanced "capitalist" societies like Japan and Germany, and even less so in the one advanced "noncapitalist" society, the Soviet Union. Thus, for Utopians, the United States is the paradigmatic revolutionary society in the world. While a number of "loud" but more backward revolutions are occurring elsewhere, the real, most advanced, but "silent," revolution is taking place in the United States. For better or for worse, the whole case for technological Utopianism rests on the analysis of present trends and conditions in the United States. Is the United States undergoing a postindustrial revolution in technology, and is this revolution setting the stage, as many Utopians claim, for the ultimate elimination of scarcity, and with this the elimination of every major social problem? At this particular time, with rampant pessimism and fatalism having replaced the optimism of the 1960s, the Utopian conception of contemporary America may seem wholly implausible. But to make sure, we had better still take a closer look at the Utopian argument.

Conclusion

In this chapter, I have summarized what I think is the best argument for the Utopian view by breaking it down into the following four premises:

Premise 1: We are presently undergoing a postindustrial revolution in technology

Premise 2: In the postindustrial age, technological growth will be sustained

Premise 3: In the postindustrial age, continued technological growth will lead to the elimination of economic scarcity

Premise 4: The elimination of economic scarcity will lead to the elimination of every major social evil

In the remainder of part one, I will explicate each of the premises singly, and I will attempt to show why Utopians are inclined to believe them. I will not, however, be able to give a full proof for each of the premises. Each is highly speculative and is based on complicated assumptions. What I will do is analyze some key concepts or key assumptions underlying each premise; many other underlying concepts or assumptions will be left out. In the next chapter, I will discuss the first two, less controversial, premises; I will focus mainly on the concepts of technology, technological growth, and postindustrial technology. In chapter 4, I will analyze one key assumption underlying the third premise; this is the assumption that the postindustrial revolution in technology will transform capitalist (and socialist) power structures into technocratic power structures (and thereby facilitate the struggle against scarcity). In chapter 5, I will analyze one key assumption underlying the fourth premise. According to many, most social evils derive from human aggression. I will ask whether it is reasonable to believe that the elimination of scarcity will lead to the elimination of human aggression.

Notes

[1]Theodore Roszak, *The Making of a Counter-Culture* (Garden City: Doubleday, 1967), p. 11. Emphasis added.

[2]C. West Churchman, *The Systems Approach* (New York: Dell, 1968), pp. 3–4.

[3]Arthur Clarke, *Profiles of the Future* (New York: Bantam, 1964), pp. 161–162.

[4]John Maynard Keynes, "Economic Possibilities for Our Grandchildren," in *Essays in Persuasion* (London: Macmillan, 1972), p. 329.

[5]Ibid., pp. 330–331.

[6]R. Buckminster Fuller, *Utopia or Oblivion: The Prospects for Humanity* (New York: Bantam, 1969).

[7]Ibid., p. 290.

[8]Ibid., p. 291.

[9]Keynes, "Economic Possibilities," p. 326.

[10]R. Buckminster Fuller, *Earth, Inc.* (Garden City: Doubleday, 1973), p. 18.

[11]Fuller, *Utopia or Oblivion*, p. 288.

[12]Clarke, *Profiles*, pp. 160–161.

[13]Herman Kahn and Anthony J. Wiener, *Year Two Thousand* (New York: Macmillan, 1967), p. 168. (I have adjusted the figures somewhat to account for inflation since 1965); also cf. *Science*, 190, No. 4,214 (Nov. 7, 1975), 540.

[14]See, for example, Norbert Wiener, *The Human Use of Human Beings* (Boston: Houghton Mifflin, 1950); Daniel Bell, *The Coming of Post-Industrial Society* (New York: Basic Books, 1973); Zbigniew Brzezinski, *Between Two Ages: America's Role in the Technetronic Era* (New York: Viking, 1970); Kenneth Boulding, *The Meaning of the Twentieth Century* (New York: Harper & Row, 1964); Alvin Toffler, *Future Shock* (New York: Bantam, 1970).

[15]Cf. Churchman, *The Systems Approach*; Bell, *The Coming of Post-Industrial Society*; Fuller, *Utopian or Oblivion*; especially, John Kenneth Galbraith, *The New Industrial State* (New York: New American Library, 1967).

3

Technology, Growth, and the Postindustrial Revolution

Let us begin by discussing the two premises of the Utopians' argument that seem most plausible and that can be most readily conceded to them. These are the premises (1) that advanced societies, with the United States at the forefront, are undergoing a postindustrial revolution in technology, and (2) that technology, in the postindustrial age, will continue to enjoy sustained growth. Let us focus especially on the key concepts of *technology*, *technological growth*, and *postindustrial revolution*, all of which are operative in these premises.

Technology

What is technology? In the broadest sense, it is any kind of practical know-how. So conceived, technology is involved in all human activity, for all human activity involves practical know-how. There is a technology for playing poker, scoring touchdowns, having successful sex, winning at politics, getting along with people, and performing religious rituals. However, so defined, the term "technology" is misleading and is of little use to us. It forces us indiscriminately to examine all types of human practice. It fails to set off any clearly defined subsector of human activity which can be contrasted with others and whose influence on the others can be determined. Finally, it leads us to lump under one heading types of phenomena which are more dissimilar than similar, and which do not really belong together.

More often, when people use the word "technology," they have in mind only certain kinds of practical know-how—namely, those involved in production. As one author puts it, "Technology is society's pool of knowledge regarding the industrial arts."[1] Technology is knowing how to produce more and better out of less. For our purposes, then, technology will be defined, more restrictedly, as follows: *A technology is any systematized practical knowledge, based on experimentation and/or scientific theory, which enhances the capacity of society to produce goods and services, and which is embodied in productive skills, organization, or machinery.*

This definition clearly sets technology off from other kinds of practical know-how. It excludes, for example, the skills of priests and medicine men, which are based on faith or mysticism rather than science or practical experience. It excludes productively useless skills, such as the ability to crack one's knuckles or to memorize phone books, or expertise in monopoly or handball. Finally, the definition excludes any productivity relevant know-how which is not embodied in production skills, organization, or machinery. Though some ancient Greeks had, in a vague way, discovered the principle of the steam engine, the credit for the introduction of steam technology goes not to them but to eighteenth-century English craftsmen (such as Thomas Newcomen and James Watt). The latter were able to do what the former could not, namely, translate these vague principles into productive skills and machinery.

However, the above definition, though restrictive, goes beyond those excessively narrow conceptions of technology which identify it exclusively with tools, machinery, and other productive hardwares. Technology is not a set of things. Rather, it is an abstract system of practical knowledge, which often, but not always, finds its embodiment in productive hardware. Indeed, many important innovations in technology, such as the medieval three-field system of agriculture and the modern division of labor in the factory, have involved little or no changes in tools or machinery. In the three-field system, one field grows winter crop (perhaps wheat), a second grows spring crop (say, either barley or legumes), and a third lies fallow; crops are rotated yearly, giving each field a turn at growing the winter crop, the spring crop, and lying fallow. The introduction of the three-field system greatly increased the productivity of medieval agriculture, yet it was unaccompanied by any changes in productive hardware.

The introduction of the division of labor within the factory did the same for manufacture. Previously, each worker would perform all the operations required to produce a manufactured good. Each pin maker, for example, would lengthen the wire, sharpen one end, shape the head at the other end, and carry out the remaining twenty or so operations involved in making pins. Then it was discovered that the capacity of society to produce pins would be greatly enhanced if each worker repeatedly performed only a few of the required operations. Some workers specialized in stretching the wire, some in sharpening one end, some in shaping the head, and some in packaging the final product. Though a significant technological innovation, the introduction of the division of labor within each industry involved little or no changes in productive hardware. Technological change often takes the form of improvements in skills and organization of work, rather than in tools or machinery.

Technological Growth

Utopians believe in continuous and indefinite technological growth. Can this belief be defended? To find out, we need first to get a clearer idea of technological growth.

What is technological growth, and how can it be measured? From our definition of technology, it follows that there is technological growth when the system of production generates a larger or better output from the same amount of input; technological growth occurs when the quality or quantity of output per unit input improves or increases. The output in this case is whatever is produced. The "unit input" is usually (but not always) identified as "a man-hour of labor." For practical purposes, we can assume that technological growth is equivalent to increase in the quantity of the product, or improvement in its quality, per man-hour of labor. If one hour of one worker's labor can produce this year more razor blades, or better razor blades, than it could last year, then we can assume that the technology of razor blade production has grown in the past year. Unfortunately, though it is fairly easy to measure increases in the quantity of output, there is no known or accepted way of measuring an improvement of the quality of output. For this reason, statisticians completely disregard qualitative improvement and focus exclusively on quantitative increases when attempting to measure technological growth. They tend to measure technological growth purely in terms of increasing labor productivity, that is, the increasing quantity of product per man-hour of labor. For example, improvements in the quality of razor blades produced by one hour of one laborer's work do not appear in the usual measures of growth of razor blade technology; only increases in the quantity of razor blades per man-hour find their way into the statisticians' reports.

Thus, some technological growth, when it leads to qualitative improvements in the output can occur without any corresponding increase in labor productivity. Conversely, some increases in labor productivity occur without any corresponding growth in technology. Labor productivity will increase if workers are merely given more tools and machines to work with, and it will increase if workers are forced to speed up or otherwise intensify their work (as when the speed of the assembly line is increased). In neither of these cases do increases in labor productivity follow upon growth in technology.

Nonetheless, despite these imperfections, growth in labor productivity remains the most convenient indicator of technological growth. It usually, though not always, provides a fair estimate of the quantitative aspects of technological growth. (The qualitative aspects at this time seem impossible to measure.)[2]

The Future of Technological Growth

During the past few centuries, labor productivity in the West (Europe and North America) has been increasing at a rate of approximately 2 percent per year. It seems reasonable to assume that technology has been growing at a comparable rate during the same period. Such being the case, the Utopian claim that the technology of the future will enjoy a sustained growth has some basis in past performance. It seems plausible that technology will continue to do in the future what it has done in the past.[3]

However, we must remember that in the broadest historical perspective such sustained growth has been the exception rather than the rule. It is a very recent phenomenon, dating only to the industrial revolution in eighteenth-century Europe. In preindustrial societies, the rule was stagnation rather than growth in technology. The first great technological breakthrough in human history is the emergence of primitive hunting technology involving simple stone tools. But the next stage in the history of technology, the agricultural revolution, did not automatically follow. Most hunting societies persisted indefinitely in their own ways and only a few made the leap into agricultural technology; the former stagnated in isolation or were eliminated by their more productive neighbors. There were in turn many stages in the development of agricultural technology, beginning with simple garden tools and horticultural techniques, and ending with large-scale farming with heavy plows, domesticated beasts of burden, crop rotation, flood control, and irrigation. The pathway from a low agricultural to a high agricultural stage was again taken by very few societies over very long periods—the latter being interspersed with long intervals of stagnation and regression. And very few of these agriculturally successful societies were in turn able or disposed to make the next step into industrial technology. China is an interesting case in point. Chinese technology blossomed in the first fourteen centuries A.D. and was consistently ahead of European technology by three or four centuries. China gets credit for having first developed gunpowder, the magnetic compass, the mechanical clock, primitive printing presses, the horse collar, the stirrup, and suspension bridges. By the eleventh century, the Chinese were already making full use of coal and coke in sophisticated metallurgical processes and had already introduced advanced machinery in textiles production. In short, they had within their grasp the technical wherewithal for a major industrial revolution. But the leap was never made; the nascent industrial revolution was aborted. By the seventeenth century, Chinese technology began to stagnate and to fall decidedly behind that of the West.[4]

Consequently, it seems wrong to attribute to technology any magical propensity for self-propagation or self-development. Whether or not technology grows systematically depends, in a way yet to be understood, on the institutional framework and the cultural and intellectual milieu within which it operates, and on the resources and wealth available to it. Apparently only in industrial (or postindustrial) societies have all these factors been favorable to sustained technological growth. With industrialization came a group of institutions altogether committed to economic growth and rational planning, and adequately supplied with the savings needed to fund the technological innovations required by these economic imperatives. And also, very importantly, it was only with the coming of industrialization that science and technology became sufficiently mature to interlock in such a way that scientific development could be used systematically to generate technological development, and technological development in turn could be used to generate further scientific development. Before the industrial revolution, science and technology interacted only sporadically. Technology, being coterminous with the whole of human history, antedated science and normally developed quite independently of it. It should be no surprise that, in the preindustrial world, scientific growth was often accompanied by technological stagnation (as in ancient Greece) or that a high point for technological development could also be a low point for science (as in medieval Europe). And it should be no surprise that such great technical architects of the industrial revolution (as Watt) were either blithely ignorant of or indifferent to current developments in physics and chemistry. Indeed, far from being based on the application of any scientific theory, the invention of the steam engine was an important stimulus to the development of thermodynamics in the early nineteenth century. Since then, however, science and technology have become inextricably intertwined; and it is this positive feedback connection between them which in part accounts for the sustained growth of both.[5]

If sustained technological growth is such a comparatively recent phenomenon—that is, if in terms of the whole history of humans it has been the exception rather than the rule—then what reason could we have for believing that it can be maintained indefinitely into the future? Utopians can respond that the institutional framework and the intellectual milieu will indefinitely continue to be highly favorable for continued technological growth. This claim is no longer as plausible as it was just fifteen years ago. The enthusiasm of both the private and public sectors for subsidizing scientific and technological research has lessened significantly. The rate of growth of labor productivity has decreased and organized technology has proved more resistant to managerial control than was previously believed. But even if all institutions were favorable, technology might still founder because of its own limitations. It is arguable that there are upper limits to technological growth, or that sustained research in technology will yield diminishing returns. It is highly probable that the present pace of exponential growth in technology cannot be maintained forever. This is glaringly obvious in fields such as transportation. In one century, the maximum speed of various modes of transportation was raised from less than seventy miles per hour (before our earliest locomotives) to four thousand miles per hour (rocket planes). This rate of development cannot be maintained very much longer, and even if it could, there would come a time when further increases would have little social value. What is true of transportation is also true of communications and military technology.[6]

However, an indefinite growth of technology at the present rate does not have to be part of the Utopian view so long as the need for an indefinite high rate of social progress is not also part of that view. And there is no reason why it should be. To bring about needed social progress is to bring about the attenuation or elimination of major social problems or evils. It can be maintained quite plausibly that our social problems or ills are finite and therefore can be resolved in a finite time. Thus, the more social progress there is, the less social progress is needed. Presumably, after a period of continued progress the problem of scarcity and with it all the other major social problems will have been resolved. At this stage, no more major social progress will be needed, though some minor improvements might be welcome. For this reason, Utopians do not have to commit themselves to indefinite growth in technology. All they need to say is that technology will continue to grow long enough to generate the necessary and sufficient conditions for the elimination of scarcity, and therewith all major social problems.

Whether the sustained growth of technology can continue at least for the foreseeable future depends in part on the nature of the new technology and the opportunities which it will provide. To explore Utopian views about this new technology, we turn to the concept of the postindustrial revolution.

Postindustrial Technology

In 1950, Norbert Wiener, the father of cybernetics, heralded the coming of a "Second Industrial Revolution," spearheaded by the development of the computer and other communications systems, and buttressed by breakthroughs in electronics. This spurred a bevy of Utopians to predict the onset of a postindustrial era in technology.[7] Let us see if this belief is plausible.

No doubt it is easy to document and dramatize technological innovations in a world in which technological growth has been institutionalized. And there have been piles of innovations since World War II, as there also were before World War II. But it is not easy to show which among all these innovations constitute major transformations or revolutions in technology. Particularly, it is not easy to distinguish those developments in technology which are still part of the framework of industrial technology from those which go beyond industrial technology. After all, since the advent of industrial technology (the steam engine and the mechanization of materials-processing in the textile industry) there have been continued breakthroughs in technology. The internal combustion engine, steam turbines, hydroelectric power, the electric light, the telephone, the radio, and atomic power are but some of the most notable. But none of these are now construed as having constituted a second industrial revolution or as having ushered in a postindustrial era in technology; they are seen as logical extensions of industrial technology rather than as transitions into postindustrial technology.

What is it that distinguishes modern computer and communications systems from the earlier kinds of technological innovations (such as the automobile and the atom bomb) that allow the former but not the latter to be called postindustrial (rather than industrial) technologies? In what sense is the introduction of computer, communications, behavioral, and managerial technologies to count as a major revolution in technology, while the invention of the internal combustion engine and the atomic power plant counted only as important developments within an already existing type of technology (that is, industrial technology)?

The answers usually given to this and similar questions by the prophets of the postindustrial revolution tend unfortunately to be vague and incomplete. But perhaps we can determine what a good answer would be. We know that the transition from agrarian technology to industrial technology in the eighteenth century is certainly one of the major technological revolutions in the history of humankind, next only to the first agricultural revolution. If anything is to count as a major revolution in technology, it is the industrial revolution, this emergence of industrial technology. Those who are telling us that we are undergoing a postindustrial revolution in technology are suggesting that we are undergoing a change in technology which is as momentous and impactful as the original industrial revolution. By telling us that we are moving from the industrial to the postindustrial age, they are claiming that we are experiencing a transition of the same magnitude and scope as the earlier transition from the age of agrarian technology to the age of industrial technology.

Now we have a clue for ascertaining the contrast between industrial and postindustrial technology. Whatever it is, it must be of the same magnitude and scope as the contrast between agrarian and industrial technology. But how is preindustrial agrarian technology to be differentiated from industrial technology?

Technology is any practical knowledge embodied in production. Changes in the development of technology can only be measured by reference to the impact which these changes have on the system of production. Only a development in technology which has a very large impact on production can be labeled a revolution in technology. But a technological change can have an impact on production in many ways. It can bring about significant changes in the outputs of production (e.g., the amounts and kinds of goods and services), in the inputs or factors of production (e.g., land and capital), or in the processes of production. (Within the processes of production, changes in technology can affect the organization of production, the level of worker skills or the types of instruments or machinery.) So a major transformation in technology will typically involve a major increase in the outputs of production, a major shift in the kind of goods produced, a major shift in the primary factor of production, a revolution in the organization of production, in the function of the worker, and/or in the type of instruments used. Thus, we have at least six categories in terms of which the major stages in the history of technology can be differentiated:

1. Level of productivity
2. Principal product
3. Principal factor of production
4. Organization of production
5. Function of the worker
6. Type of instrument

A major change in each of these categories seems to have accompanied the transition from agrarian technology to industrial technology. So, if we are really undergoing a major transition from industrial to postindustrial technology, then we should be experiencing changes in the above six categories that parallel in amplitude and importance the changes that took place in these categories during the industrial revolution. Let us see if this is so.

CHANGES IN THE LEVEL OF PRODUCTIVITY

Labor productivity in preindustrial agrarian societies is quite low and does not tend to increase. It rarely supports per capita incomes exceeding $300. In industrial societies, labor productivity is dramatically higher; it supports per capita incomes of up to $4,000. And, as we have seen, it grows sustainedly at a rate of approximately 2 percent per year.

In the light of this, it is reasonable to believe that the United States is entering a postindustrial age in technology, if it is reasonable as well to believe that the United States is experiencing a significant increase in the growth rate of labor productivity, leading to new qualitative levels of affluence. Can this be claimed? The data are quite mixed. On the one hand, it has been noted that the rate of growth of labor productivity rose to 3.2 percent per year between 1947 and 1965. This has led some optimists to project a labor productivity growth rate for the United States of 4 percent during the closing decades of the twentieth century, and a resulting per capita gross national product of at least $17,000 by the year 2000. However, these recent increases in the labor productivity growth rate were due primarily to agriculture and not to modern industry; they may reflect only a temporary burst, rather than a long-term trend.[8] Meanwhile, the United States economy is now suffering serious dislocations, hampering the growth of productivity, and consequently also the growth of per capita income.

Thus if the emergence of a postindustrial age in technology is tied to changes in the growth rate of labor productivity and achievement of different qualitative levels of affluence, then it is not yet obvious that we have entered such an age.

CHANGES IN THE TYPE OF PRODUCT

To put it simply, the technology of an agrarian society is devoted mainly to the production of foodstuffs, while that of industrial societies is devoted mainly to the production of manufactured goods. For example, 90 percent of all British workers were involved in agricultural production in the year 1700, whereas today only 5 percent are. If agrarian technology is identified mainly with the production of foodstuffs, and industrial technology with the production of manufactured goods, then postindustrial technology may be identified primarily with the production of services, as in the areas of health and education.

And indeed the prophets of postindustrialization are claiming that the United States has become primarily a service economy; they maintain that by 1968, 64 percent of the American work force was engaged in the production of services. But here we must be careful. That the service sector has the largest work force does not necessarily make it the most important productive sector. This fact could simply reflect the relative low productivity of the service sector; it takes more labor to produce the same dollar value in the service sector than it does in the goods sector. To claim that the service sector has become the most important economic sector is to claim not only that it employs the most workers, but also that it produces the most value (as measured in dollars).[9]

SHIFTS IN THE PRIMARY FACTORS OF PRODUCTION

In agrarian societies, land is the primary factor or input of production to which technology is applied; in industrial societies, inanimate capital (such as machinery) is the primary factor or input of production to which technology is applied. What factor of production looms most importantly in postindustrial societies? Such postindustrial theorists (as John Kenneth Galbraith) have argued that human expertise (often referred to as "human capital") is playing the same primary role for postindustrial technology that land played for agrarian technology and inanimate capital played for industrial technology. This view is supported by two facts. First, the rate of growth of investment in the development and maintenance of human expertise is greatly outpacing the rate of growth in investment in inanimate capital. For example, in 1921 expenditures for research and development constituted only 0.2 percent of the United States gross national product, whereas by 1961 it constituted nearly 3 percent. Second, though increases in capital and labor were the major contributors to economic growth at the height of the industrial revolution, increased education and knowledge are now seen as the major contributors to economic growth.[10]

CHANGES IN THE ORGANIZATION OF PRODUCTION

It could be argued that, at least in preindustrial agrarian societies of the West, the household constituted the major unit for production and economic planning. For example, the production of textiles was planned and carried out in cottages by families and apprentices. With the advent of the industrial revolution, the large factory became the primary unit for planning and production, while the nation's economy as a whole was subject to the unplanned anarchism of the competitive market. The next logical step beyond the factory in the organization of production is the subjection of large geographical regions to integrated economic planning. The rise of monopolies, oligopolies, and the welfare state has provided the basis for national and international integration of all stages of the production process, from the extraction of resources to the marketing of finished products. It has provided the basis for controlling the ups and downs of national and international economies. Overall, it has paved the way for the subjection of whole national and international economies to unified technical control. While this trend has been in large part a political one, it could not have taken place without major developments in organizational technology (such as those in applied economics, managerial technology, and systems design), as well as behavioral technology (such as advertising techniques and industrial psychology).

If agrarian technology in the West is associated with the household as the major economic planning unit, and industrial technology with the factory system, then postindustrial technology can be associated with integrated nationwide (or worldwide) economic planning. So conceived, postindustrial technology has taken root in the organizational and behavioral sciences.

CHANGES IN THE ROLE OF THE WORKER

With respect to this classification, the distinction between agrarian and industrial technology is quite straightforward. Agrarian production is essentially crafts production with the worker functioning as a skilled artisan, whereas industrial production is mechanized production with the worker functioning as a machine operator. Is there room for another type of worker function, to be associated with postindustrial technology?

Production may be broken down into four elements: the power source, the processing of materials (the transformation of raw materials into finished products), the handling of materials (the transferring of materials from stage to stage), and the control procedures (checking for quality, correcting errors, supervising and so on). In agrarian production, the power source is animate (human or animal muscle power), the processing procedures involve simple tools, and both materials handling and controls are carried out completely by humans. In industrial production, the power source is inanimate (for instance water, steam, or atomic power), and the processing procedures are carried out by low-speed, special-purpose machines (such as spinning jennies and looms). However, at the industrial stage, materials handling is only at the lower level of mechanization (such as the conveyer belt) and control is completely carried out by human beings. This leaves room for a major transformation in the processes of production and the role of the worker beyond industrialization. In this new form, not only are the power sources inanimate and the processing procedures governed by multipurpose, high-speed machines, but the materials-handling procedures and control procedures are largely automatic. For example, in oil refineries and chemical firms the automatically processed materials are conveyed mechanically from one stage of production to the next; for the most part, the quality of the products is checked automatically and errors are corrected automatically. The function of workers is merely to repair the machinery and to take care of errors not corrected by the machinery. This is an example of automated production, in which the worker functions primarily as a machine monitor.

Thus it seems possible to distinguish between three major stages in the development of worker functions correlated with agrarian, industrial, and postindustrial technologies. Crafts production, where the worker functions as a skilled artisan, is correlated with agrarian technology; mechanized production (as in textiles) where the worker functions as a machine operator, is correlated with industrial technology, and automated production, where the worker functions as a machine monitor, is associated with postindustrial technology.[11]

CHANGES IN INSTRUMENTS OR MACHINES

The technology of any period is embodied in tools and mechanisms which function as extensions and simulators of, or replacements for, certain key human or animal organs involved directly or indirectly in the production process. For example, the shovel is an extension of the human arm and the wheel a replacement for human legs. Particular types of technology may be distinguished in terms of the types of organs which the mechanisms generated by these technologies tend to simulate or to replace. Thus, agrarian technology is embodied in mechanisms which function mainly as extensions or replacements of human or animal limbs such as the arm or the leg, while industrial technology is embodied in mechanisms which function mainly as replacements for human or animal muscle power. Agrarian technology has generated the heavy plow, the stirrup, and the javelin, while industrial technology has generated the steam engine and the atomic power plant. However, agrarian and industrial instrumentation or machinery, when taken together, replace a very small sector of human or animal physiological activity.

Central brain processes, as well as peripheral perceptual processes (such as that of the eyes or ears) remain unsimulated or unreplaced; this means that all the physiological activities involving the gathering, filtering, processing, storing, and retrieval of information remain unmechanized at the stage of industrialization. The emergence of postindustrial technology could thus be equated with the emergence of a new informational technology which ultimately replaces or simulates the role of the human brain and human perceptual organs in the productive process. Postindustrial technology is thus embodied in information-gathering devices such as radar and sonar, in information-processing and storing devices such as the computer, in information-transmitting devices such as television, and in information-control devices such as the future mechanisms for genetic engineering and behavior control.

The three major types of technology can be distinguished in terms of the types of instruments or machines in which they are embodied, once the latter are classified in terms of the human or animal organs which they extend, simulate, or replace in the productive process. Agrarian technology is embodied in instruments which extend or replace human limbs, industrial technology in machines which replace animal muscle power, and postindustrial technology in machines which simulate or replace the human brain and sense receptors. Agrarian technology is a tool-oriented technology, industrial technology a power technology, and postindustrial technology an informational technology.

SUMMARY

We can reasonably conclude that the United States and other advanced societies are making a transition from the industrial age to the postindustrial age in technology if we find that all or most of the following conditions hold: (1) the rate of growth of labor productivity has risen from 2 percent to 3–4 percent—and as a consequence, the economy is moving toward a $17,000 per capita income by the end of the century; (2) the primary outputs of the system of production are services rather than manufactured goods; (3) the primary factor of production is human expertise rather than inanimate capital; (4) the primary unit of productive planning is the integrated national or world economy, rather than the individual firm; (5) workers increasingly are functioning as machine monitors rather than machine operators—that is, automation is replacing mechanization; (6) the major new machine technologies are, for the most part, informational technologies rather than power technologies.

Table 3.1 summarizes the major differences among agrarian, industrial, and postindustrial technologies.

Conclusion

In this chapter, we have studied the underlying concepts of the two least controversial premises of the Utopian argument. Each of these premises seems quite plausible and might well be conceded by Dystopians, Socialists, and other opponents of the Utopian view. There is good evidence for saying that advanced societies are entering some sort

Table 3.1
DIFFERENCES AMONG AGRARIAN, INDUSTRIAL, AND
POSTINDUSTRIAL TECHNOLOGIES

Aspect of Technology Affected	*Agrarian*	*Industrial*	*Postindustrial*
Level of productivity	Supports less than $300 in per capita income	Supports up to $4,000 in per capita income; grows at approximately 2 percent yearly	Supports up to $17,000 in per capita income; grows at 3–4 percent yearly
Primary product	Food	Manufactured goods	Services
Primary factor of production	Land	Capital	Human expertise
Organization of production	Household	Factory	Integrated nationwide and worldwide economic planning; development of organizational and behavioral technologies
Role of the worker	Crafts production; worker as skilled artisan	Mechanized Production; worker as machine operator	Automated production; worker as machine monitor
Instruments and machinery	Tool-oriented technology; instrument as extensions of, or replacements for, human limbs	Power technology; machines as replacements for human or animal muscle power	Informational technology; machines as replacements for human brains or sensory receptors

of postindustrial age in technology. Automation and informational technology are clearly on the rise. Economies are increasingly being subject to integrated, technical planning. Societies have intensified their investment in human expertise. The evidence is somewhat less strong that modern economies are primarily service economies, or that the rate of long-term productivity growth has increased substantially.

It also seems reasonable to believe that technology in the postindustrial age will exhibit sustained growth. After all, technology has been growing for several centuries, and postindustrialization does not seem to have undermined the institutional and cultural incentives for growth. Rather, the introduction of informational technology, the stress on human expertise, the perfection of planning techniques, and the trend toward automation all clearly create new opportunities for productivity growth and hence technological growth. Indeed, they may well set the stage for unprecedented high rates of technological growth.

Notes

[1] Edwin Manfield, *The Economics of Technological Change* (New York: Norton, 1968), p. 10.

[2] Ibid., pp. 10–42.

[3] Ibid., pp. 22–29; Daniel Bell, *The Coming of Post-Industrial Society* (New York: Basic Books, 1973), pp. 193–195.

[4] Cf. Joseph Needham, "Science and China's Influence on the World," in *The Grand Titration* (Toronto: University of Toronto Press, 1970), pp. 55–122; Mark Elvin, *The Pattern of the Chinese Past* (Palo Alto, Calif.: Stanford U. Press, 1973); John U. Nef, *The Conquest of the Material World* (New York: Meridian, 1967), p. 134n.

[5] Cf. Lynn White, Jr., *Medieval Technology and Social Change* (London: Oxford, 1962); John F. Sandfort, *Heat Engines* (Garden City: Doubleday, 1962).

[6] Stuart Chase, *The Most Probable World* (Baltimore: Pelican, 1969), p. 19.

[7] In addition to Wiener, *The Human Use of Human Beings* (Boston: Houghton Mifflin, 1950), cf. Daniel Bell, *The Coming of Post-Industrial Society* (New York: Basic Books, 1973); Herman Kahn and Anthony J. Weiner, *Year Two Thousand* (New York: Macmillan, 1967); Zbigniew Brzezinski, *Between Two Ages: America's Role in the Technetronic Era* (New York: Viking, 1970); Alvin Toffler, *Future Shock* (New York: Bantam, 1970); J. J. Servan-Schreiber, *The American Challenge* (New York: Avon, 1967); William Faunce, *Problems of an Industrial Society* (New York: McGraw-Hill, 1968); and Kenneth Boulding, *The Meaning of the Twentieth Century* (New York: Harper & Row, 1964).

[8] Herman Kahn and Anthony Wiener, *Year Two Thousand* (New York: Macmillan, 1967); pp. 119, 123–127, 161, 168); Bell, *Coming*, p. 195.

[9]Bell, *Coming*, pp. 124, 132, 134; Eli Ginzberg, *Manpower Agenda for America* (New York: McGraw-Hill, 1968), pp. 38–52.

[10]Richard Nelson, Merton J. Peck, and Edward Kalachek, *Technology, Economic Growth, and Public Policy* (Washington, D.C.: Brookings Institution, 1967), p. 46; Edward Shapiro, *Macroeconomic Analysis*, (New York: Harcourt, Brace, 1970), pp. 460–465.

[11]Faunce, *Problems*, p. 48.

4

Technocracy: The Silent Transition

Postindustrial Technology and Postscarcity

We now turn to the more controversial premises of the Utopian argument. In this chapter, we look at some of the assumptions underlying the premise that technological growth, in the postindustrial age, will lead to the elimination of scarcity. In the next chapter, we look at some of the assumptions underlying the premise that the elimination of scarcity will lead to the elimination of all other major social problems.

Do we have any reason for believing that postindustrial technology will bring about the end of scarcity? Why should we reasonably expect postindustrial technology to be able to do what industrial technology was unable to do? Isn't it unrealistic to believe that scarcity can ever be eliminated? Let us see how Utopians might answer these questions.

In fairness to Utopians, we should concede that initially the burden of proof is on our—not their—shoulders. For if everything else were equal, indefinite technological growth would lead to the elimination of scarcity. (By "everything else is equal" I mean that there are no counteracting causes.) Technological growth normally takes the form of increases in the productivity of workers. But if everything else is equal, greater productivity entails greater total production. Furthermore, if everything else is equal, greater production means greater satisfaction of wants and needs, and hence less scarcity. So if everything else is equal, sustained technological growth entails sustained proportional decreases in scarcity; ultimately, it entails the elimination of scarcity.

But, of course, not everything has been equal in the period of industrial technological growth in America and elsewhere. Because of important counteracting trends, industrial technological growth has failed decisively to bring about proportional decreases in scarcity. As technology and production have grown in the industrial West, so have the numbers of the poor, those who lack the economic wherewithal to satisfy their minimal survival needs. Furthermore, increased production of artificial goods has been accompanied by increased depletion of such natural goods as clean air and water and of nonrenewable mineral resources. Finally, growing production has been correlated with growing needs and wants, such as the need for TV sets and automobiles. In the age of industrial technology, all these trends have tended to counteract the scarcity-reducing effects of technological growth.

Is there any hope that these counteracting trends will be eliminated or greatly reduced by the advent of the postindustrial age in technology? Why should postindustrial technology be able to eliminate, or greatly reduce, poverty, inequality, pollution, resource depletion, and the growth of consumer wants when industrial technology has been unable to do so?

The Utopian can deal with this challenge in two ways. He or she might simply blame these counteracting trends on the peculiarities of industrial technology itself. There is some sense to this. For example, industrial technology, insofar as it is associated with the production of tangible goods rather than services, intensifies the problems of pollution and resource depletion. Also, since industrial technology has not developed the techniques of system-wide planning, it cannot easily be used to eliminate unwanted and unplanned byproducts such as environmental disruption. In addition, industrial technology has significantly increased the gap between skilled and unskilled workers, between mental and physical work, and between various kinds of skilled work; it has thrived on bureaucratic hierarchy with orders coming down from the top. It has therefore reinforced extreme inequality in income, and with it, poverty. Finally, the growth of industrial technology has depended on growth in investment and hence growth in production; but indefinite growth in production seems to presuppose growth in wants and needs. Now, the Utopian may argue that postindustrial technology will tend to be environmentally less disruptive since it has developed special techniques of systems planning enabling it to take into consideration all of the consequences of production. Postindustrial technology may significantly decrease poverty and income inequality by virtually eliminating unskilled work and by greatly reducing the gap between mental and physical work. And some have maintained (as has Alvin Toffler) that postindustrial technology, as an information technology, will undermine bureaucratic inequality by allowing for two-way and decentralized information flow. Finally, the Utopian might argue that in the age of postindustrial affluence growth in technology will not be so dependent on growth in production, and hence on indefinite growth in wants and needs.

This is all fine and good; industrial technology does seem to have contributed somewhat to growth in the numbers of the poor, to inequality, to environmental disruption, and to growth in consumer wants. But surely it is not primarily to blame for these counteracting trends. It is arguable that, compatibly with industrial technology, we in America might have had less poverty, inequality, environmental disruption, and compulsive growth in wants had we organized our economic and political institutions differently. Many of our problems and successes come from the fact that ours has been a capitalist society rather than from the fact that ours has been an industrial society. Because they owned and controlled our industrial technology, capitalists appropriated a disproportionate share of the product of that technology; poverty and inequality were the inevitable consequences. Because they operated in a private market economy, capitalists did not have to pay for the social costs (in the form of pollution, etc.) of their production processes and products; environmental disintegration was the inevitable result. Because they operated in a competitive economic system, capitalists were forced to pursue corporate growth in order to survive; the headlong growth of consumer wants (compulsive consumption) was the inevitable result. Thus capitalism seems just as responsible as industrial technology for creating obstacles to the elimination of scarcity. It is not merely industrial technology, but also the capitalist uses of industrial technology that account for the levels of poverty, environmental breakdown, and compulsive consumerism in advanced Western societies.

Utopians are now faced with the challenge of how obstacles to the elimination of scarcity generated by capitalism in the industrial age can be eliminated in the postindustrial age. How can a mere change in technology eliminate obstacles for which the previous technology was only partially responsible? This calls for a response by Utopians quite different from that so far presented. Here, Utopians must "bite the bullet." They must be willing to say that the emergence of postindustrial technology is bringing about the elimination of capitalism as we know it. How else could postindustrial technology eliminate evils systematically caused by capitalism which obstruct rapid and proportional decreases in scarcity? Not all real-life Utopians have been willing to make this claim; but some have (such as John Kenneth Galbraith, Daniel Bell, B. F. Skinner, Arthur Clarke), though they may have "fudged" somewhat.

To summarize: postindustrial technology can lead to the elimination of scarcity within the foreseeable future only if its growth causes proportional decreases in scarcity. But growth in technology can only bring about proportional decreases in scarcity if certain counteracting trends (such as increasing poverty, extreme inequality, increasing pollution and resource depletion, and growing wants and needs) are eliminated or significantly reduced. So postindustrial technology can put us full-speed on the road to postscarcity only if it greatly reduces or eliminates these counteracting trends. But these counteracting trends, in the modern Western world, have been reinforced primarily by the imperatives of industrialization and capitalism. Hence postindustrial technology can greatly reduce or eliminate these counteracting trends only if it does not share those traits of industrial technology which reinforce these trends and only if it leads to the elimination of capitalism. The Utopian can argue, with some plausibility, that postindustrial technology is different enough from industrial technology not to share its scarcity-inducing traits. But can the Utopian argue with any plausibility that postindustrial technology is powerful enough to eliminate capitalism in the advanced West and, especially, in America? To this question we now turn.

Technocracy

Surprisingly, a significant number of theorists, Utopian and otherwise, have argued that the "new" technology (postindustrial or whatever) is bringing about, or has brought about, the elimination of capitalism in the United States. A. A. Berle and G. C. Means were the first to propound this; they were followed by James Burnham, and to a lesser extent by Daniel Bell, Herbert Marcuse, and Theodore Roszak. However, John Kenneth Galbraith, in his stimulating *The New Industrial State*, has made the best case for this claim.

But what has this elimination of capitalism through technology consisted of? Capitalism is any market economic system in which a relatively small number own and control the means of production and use this control to maximize their profits and their wealth. As an economic market system, capitalism is identified in terms of who controls the economy (the owners of capital, or capitalists) and what goals govern the economy (profit or wealth maximization for the capitalists).

There are two ways in which capitalism so characterized can be eliminated. The most obvious way is to eliminate the market and the capitalist class (and, of course, capitalist goals), as Marxist socialists promise to do. But in present postindustrial America some form of market and some capital-owning class continue to exist. Hence in the above sense of "elimination," capitalism has not been eliminated by the postindustrial revolution. However, a less radical way to eliminate capitalism is to bring it about that capitalist owners of the means of production no longer control the means of production and capitalist goals no longer govern the use of the means of production, though capitalists, their goals, and some form of market continue to exist. According to this view, the postindustrial revolution in technology is inducing the demise of capitalism by creating conditions in which power over the economy is being wrested slowly but surely from capitalist owners of the economy, and a new set of goals is supplanting the capitalist goals previously foisted on the economy. In this elimination of capitalism, capitalists are allowed to exist with their concentrated ownership but without their power, and their goals are allowed to persist but without their effectiveness. It is in this sense that Galbraith and his allies have been arguing that the new technology is bringing about the elimination of capitalism.

But if the capitalist owners no longer control the means of production, then who has the control? And if capitalist goals no longer govern the use of the means of production, then whose goals do? If postindustrial technology has deposed capitalists and their goals, then whom has it put in their place? Postindustrial technology is part of the means of production; if postindustrial technology has brought it about that capitalists no longer control the means of production, this is because postindustrial technology is too complicated and sophisticated to be controlled by its owners. Who then can control this technology if not the owners? The answer seems obvious: the technical experts who work on this technology, on the means of production, and for the owner-capitalists have now assumed power over this technology, and these means of production.

The picture is now becoming clear. Utopians are, or should be, telling us that with the advent of postindustrial technology control over the American corporation has been tranferred from the capitalist-owners of the American corporation to the expert-manager employees of the corporation, and that the goals governing the behavior of the corporation have been changed from capitalist goals to technician goals. Knowledge has replaced ownership as the source of economic power, and the goals of the knower have replaced the goals of the owner. The American economy, as a consequence of the postindustrial revolution, has been transformed from a capitalist economy (controlled by owners of capital and governed by their goals) to a technocratic economy (controlled by manager-technicians and governed by their goals). Or so Utopians would have us believe.

Is this belief reasonable? Is there any evidence supporting it? I will deal with these questions in the remainder of this chapter. In the next two sections, I will examine the evidence for the claim that, due to the postindustrial revolution, manager-technicians have wrested power over the corporate system from owner-capitalists. In the section following these two sections, I will examine the reasons behind the claim that a new set of goals—"technician" or "technocratic" goals, distinct from the capitalist goals of old—now govern the corporate system.

Technological Elites: The Primacy of Expertise

In his *The New Industrial State,* John Kenneth Galbraith gives a very persuasive defense of the view that, due to the advent of postindustrial technology, manager-technicians employed by the large corporations have wrested power over these corporations from the owners. Though he does not use the words "postindustrial technology," Galbraith clearly bases his argument for the rise of technocracy on two defining characteristics of the postindustrial age in technology: (1) the primacy of human expertise as a factor of production and (2) the centrality of economic planning. The argument based on the first is simpler, but also inferior, to that based on the second. I briefly summarize the former, and then give a detailed formulation of the latter.

We saw that for the agrarian age in technology the primary factor of production was land, for the industrial age it was inanimate capital (such as machinery), and for the postindustrial age it is human expertise (sometimes called "human capital"). According to Galbraith, whoever owns or otherwise has privileged access to the primary factor of production controls the system of production. Thus, in the agrarian age landowners controlled the economy, and in the industrial age, the owners of capital (the capitalists) controlled the economy. It would seem to follow that in the postindustrial age, the owners of expertise control the economy. Who own the existing expertise? The experts apparently, for experts are the ones who sell their expertise. So by parity of reasoning, if landowners controlled the agrarian economy, and capitalists the industrial economy, then scientific and technical experts can be expected to rule over the postindustrial economy.

Unfortunately, Galbraith's reasons for believing that economies are controlled by those who own the primary factors of production are not very powerful. He first assumes that the primary factors of production are always in relatively short supply; given the demand for them, they are more difficult to obtain than the other factors. For example, in the industrial age capital was more scarce than land or labor; it was easier to obtain land or labor by using or selling capital than to obtain capital by using land or one's labor. Galbraith then argues that the owner of a factor of production which is in short supply has sufficient bargaining power to control the economy. He thereafter goes on to claim that experts are in very short supply in postindustrial society; hence, insofar as they possess the primary factor of production (expertise) they are in a position to wrest control over the economy from the capitalists.[1]

This argument is much less persuasive now than it was at the time of the publication of Galbraith's book in 1967. For then the demand for scientific and technical experts by corporations was increasing much more rapidly than the supply. But since then there has been a dramatic reversal of this trend. Universities and technical schools continue to graduate more scientists and technicians every year; meanwhile, the demand for them has slowed appreciably. Today many scientists and technicians find themselves unemployed. So the vaunted bargaining power of scientists and technicians, due to their relative scarcity, has all but disappeared.

Technological Elites: The Centrality of Planning

Galbraith makes a much stronger case for the claim that scientists and technicians have wrested control over corporations from capitalists when he focuses on the growing importance of planning to the corporate system. His argument has two stages. First, he argues that the imperatives of modern technology commit the corporation to sophisticated, intensive, and wide-range planning. Then, he attempts to show that this sort of planning cannot be carried out unless the corporation is effectively under the control of managers and technicians rather than owners.

A corporation becomes an institution for planning when it is able to participate authoritatively in determining what is to be produced, how much of it is to be produced, and how resources are to be allocated for its production. This in turn is possible only if the corporation is able to participate authoritatively in determining the costs of its inputs and the prices of its products. That is, the corporation is able to engage in authoritative planning only to the extent that it is able to control, supercede, or act independently of the market. In a perfectly competitive market, the costs of production and the prices of its products are imposed on the corporation from the outside; as a consequence, the nature and quantity of its inputs and outputs are imposed on it from the outside. In a perfectly competitive market, the corporation is relieved of having to engage in authoritative planning; the system of costs for inputs and prices for outputs imposed by the market provide it with all the information it needs for determining what and how much it should produce. To say then that the imperatives of modern technology commit the corporate system to authoritative planning is to say that the imperatives of modern technology commit the corporate system to the abandonment of the competitive market system; it is to say that the major corporations can no longer successfully pursue or apply modern technology within the framework of the perfectly competitive market.

As an example of these developments, consider Jones, a nineteenth-century businessman who owns a bicycle and carriage shop. Supposing that he operates in a perfectly competitive market, Jones can produce efficiently and successfully with comparatively little planning. In effect, prices for his products and costs for his materials (over which he has no control) tell him what to buy and what to sell in order to make a profit. Should he concentrate on bicycles at the expense of carriages? Big bikes at the expense of small bikes? Two-wheel bikes at the expense of three-wheelers? It is by comparing the prices he can get for each of these kinds of products and the costs he has to pay for materials of each kind that he can tell where to put his productive emphasis in the most profitable way. In a sense, everything has been calculated for him by the market. If, however, Jones and Company grew into a giant monopoly or oligopoly the situation would be quite different. For then Jones would "fix" the prices of his products and control the costs of his materials. But then the market, no longer independent of Jones, would no longer be a reliable guide. Jones would have to do much more planning in such forms as marketing research.

But if the perfectly competitive market does all the calculating for the corporation, then why should the corporation abandon it for the greater uncertainties of monopoly and oligopoly planning? It would do this, obviously, to make more money, but also, as Galbraith points out, to deal with the imperatives of the new technology. The new technology transforms the perfectly competitive market from a relatively reliable instrument to a basically unreliable one. Competitive market prices only tell the corporation what its suppliers are willing to provide it with under what conditions in the short run, and what the consumers are willing to buy under what conditions in the short run. The perfectly competitive market can therefore be a reliable guide for corporate decision-making to the extent that new production projects or changes in production undertaken by the corporation require little time or fixed capital, or fixed capital that can be flexibly adapted to changing situations. These conditions failing, there ought at least to be reasonable expectations that supplier tendencies and consumer tastes will remain constant over the long run. However, given the nature and effects of contemporary productive technology, none of these conditions can be met. The time between initiation and completion of a major productive change (from drawing board to marketing), as well as the amount of inflexible, fixed capital involved in the change, is consistently increasing as technology becomes more sophisticated and thorough. And the new affluence created by modern technology makes consumer tastes considerably less predictable than they were when incomes were devoted mainly to food, shelter, and clothing. So if the competitive market system were preserved, the risks and costs would be too great to encourage the sort of investment characteristic of the large corporation and crucial for its wellbeing. The only alternative, according to Galbraith, is for the "perfectly competitive market," in which no firm has authoritative control over prices and costs, to be transformed into an "imperfectly competitive market," in which the large firm is able to participate in the authoritative determination of costs and prices. On the input side, the corporation will control its costs by buying out, or otherwise vertically integrating itself with, the firms which supply it with materials; on the output side, it will regulate consumer behavior through oligopolistic price collusion and through the impact of advertising on consumer tastes. The background assumption is that the modern, technologically sophisticated firm can only survive if it is able to anticipate future economic trends, that it can anticipate future economic trends only if it controls these trends, and that the key to the control of future economic trends is in the control over future costs and prices. Thus, according to Galbraith, modern technology requires that the large competitive firm, which acts in accordance with costs and prices imposed by the market, be transformed into a monopolistic or oligopolistic firm which, through its control over costs and prices, is able to engage in authoritative economic planning (i.e., is able to determine authoritatively how resources are to be allocated and what and how much is to be produced).[2]

Consider again the case of Jones, the bicycle and carriage maker. In the relatively simple world of the nineteenth century, he can rely on competitive market prices, however short-term their information is. For one thing he knows that consumer tastes will not change rapidly, and so he can rely on that. But even when they change, he can easily retool his shop to adapt to these changes. If the price of bikes suddenly dips and the price of carriages suddenly increases, with minimal changes in his productive machinery he can shift from the production of bikes to the production of carriages. But now suppose that Jones, basking in prosperity, sells his bicycle and carriage shop and goes into the automobile business. By 1960, Jones and Company can no longer rely on a competitive market as did its ancestor company. Suppose that Jones III wonders whether to put a small car on the market. Consumer tastes are by now complicated and unstable. So he must commission a three-year study of consumer automobile-buying tastes. Meanwhile, he must build a whole new plant, whose machinery can only be used for the building of small cars. He cannot merely rely on the price of small cars in order to make his decision, for things may change radically by the time he has his plant in operation. Rather, he and his managers must resort to very careful planning. In addition, in order to minimize risk, they (and other car companies) must exercise considerable control over the market. They must control costs (by controlling prices of materials, etc.) to ensure that the small car will remain economic; they (and other car companies) must fix the prices of their product to minimize the uncertainties of competition and to ensure an adequate rate of return; and they must saturate consumers with advertising about the practicality and stylishness of small cars.

If contemporary technology requires the advent of intensive authoritative planning within the corporation, the latter in turn requires a technological reorganization of the management work structure. In fact, it is often suggested that the impact of postindustrial technology on the work role and organization of managers and technicians rivals the impact of industrial technology on the work role and organization of manual workers. The evolution of authoritative planning in the capitalist corporation necessitates a large influx of managers, engineers, lawyers, consultants, and the like, who in turn have to be functionally integrated in a technically rational way. The consequent division of labor brings with it a set of numerous and highly refined types of expertise. No one manager or expert can either perform or comprehend even a small number of these expert functions. Thus major decisions are made by managerial teams or committees rather than by individuals. Furthermore, given the high level of training required for each of the forms of expertise, it becomes consistently less probable that the legal owners will master any of these types of managerial expertise, and impossible that they will master most. The introduction of authoritative planning within the modern corporation thus inevitably leads to the functional separation of the class of manager-technicians from the class of owners. Whereas in the days of entrepreneurial capitalism the owner was also manager and made the major corporate decisions, now the team of managers, distinct from the owners, make the major corporate decisions.[3]

However, even if it is true that the manager-technicians, as a separate group from the primary owners, make everyday corporation decisions and that the owners rarely if ever can or do interfere with these specific decisions, it does not follow that the managers thereby control the corporation. It is quite conceivable that the primary owners constitute a "leisure ruling class" within the corporation; that is, it is conceivable that their sole function is to set the goals of the corporation and to assign to the manager-technicians the task of achieving these goals. Though the owners may never be in a position to rationally object to or veto the managers' plans before enactment, they would certainly be in a position to tell after the fact whether the goals of the corporation were achieved by the enactment of these plans. Thus, the controlling power of owners would be expressed not by their ability to engage in or to obstruct everyday decisions, but rather by their ability to reward management if the corporate goals are reached and to punish management if these goals are missed. This is the objection often made by opponents of the claim that manager-technicians have wrested control of the corporation from the owners. How does Galbraith respond to it?

In various sections of *The New Industrial State*, Galbraith makes countermoves in the face of objections of the above type; I summarize them here. For the same reasons, Galbraith posits, that nonexpert owners cannot tell, before the fact, whether some managerial plan will help reach the goals which they impute to a corporation, they are not in a position after the fact to tell if the goals have been maximally reached. What owners demand of a corporation is that it maximize its (and consequently their) profits. Now, it was quite easy for the entrepreneur of a small classical firm to tell when profits were being maximized. But when a large contemporary firm makes substantial profits, how is the nonexpert owner to tell whether profits trully have been maximized? After all, profits might have been higher if management had not put so much emphasis on growth in sales or growth in research and development. In addition, profit has become an extremely complicated accounting category and is open to a number of possible interpretations; so, even for determining what is to count as profit, the nonexpert owner is dependent on the technicians (in this case, the accountants). Of course, major stockholders know when their corporation has lost a good deal of money; in such circumstances, they fire the management team with dispatch. However, large corporations that are in a position to engage in authoritative planning (i.e., that are in a position to control prices) rarely fail to make a profit, even during the periods of recession and stagnation. Thus this residual power of the owner is rarely if ever used in a given corporation.[4]

But even if the major owners of capital were able to discern quite clearly when the corporation failed to maximize profits, they would not, according to Galbraith, normally have the wherewithal to force upon management a change in direction more conducive to their aims.

There are two ways in which large holders of capital can influence or determine the effective policy of a corporation: they may exert their power either internally through the ownership of large blocks of voting stock or externally through their ability to provide large investment loans. Neither stockholders nor bankers, Galbraith argues, are any longer in a position to impose their will on managerial decision making.

According to Galbraith, the trend toward the diffusion of stock ownership continues unabated, and now in only a few major corporations does one group own enough stock to exert controlling power, even under the most generous interpretations of the amount of stock needed to exert controlling power.[5] On this he seems amply supported by a number of recent studies. Berle and Means have made a new classical study of the top 200 corporations of 1929. They assumed that a small group could control a corporation through stock ownership if it owned at least 20 percent of the outstanding stock in that corporation. Conversely, they assumed that a corporation in which no small group owned 20 percent of the stock was controlled by manager-technicians rather than owners (unless of course it was controlled by some other corporation). Of the top 200 corporations, they found that by this standard at least 44 percent were manager-controlled, and 56 percent owner-controlled. Furthermore, they found that only 11 percent of the top 200 corporations were controlled through majority stock holdings (i.e., when a small group owns over 50 percent of the stock).[6] Robert Larner duplicated this study for the top 200 corporations of 1963. He softened the criterion for controlling ownership: any corporation in which a small group owned 10 percent of the stock was, according to him, controlled by stockholders; otherwise it was under management control. Despite this more generous criterion, Larner found a striking trend away from ownership control and toward management control: 84.5 percent of the top 200 corporations, according to him, were under management control, and only 15.5 percent under owner control. That is, in 84.5 percent of the top 200 corporations no unified group owned enough stock to enforce its will on manager-technicians employed by these corporations. In addition, he found that only 2.5 percent of the top 200 corporations were controlled by majority ownership.[7] It seems to follow that, with few remaining exceptions, individual groups of stockholders no longer have the economic wherewithal to exercise control over the corporation; manager-technicians would then naturally step into the vacuum.

But perhaps if inside capitalists (stockholders) no longer control the corporation, then outside capitalists (bankers) still do. Presumably, large firms are always in need of investment loans, and bankers in return for these loans can impose changes in managerial policy and planning. (Think of how the Mellon Bank of Pittsburgh took over Gulf Oil many decades ago.) Galbraith concedes, as he must, that when capital was scarce, bankers were quite free to impose their will on the corporations receiving their loans. But he maintains that bankers have since lost their special position of power because capital has become plentiful, if not overabundant. He argues that the corporations themselves now generate a large part of their needed investment capital. Corporations, he maintains, are now the biggest savers in the country; businesses plow a larger percentage of their profits back into the company, and allow a smaller percentage to be distributed as dividends, than they did before World War II.[8] Thus, since corporations can generate most of their investment capital, they no longer are dependent on banks and need no longer submit to their demands. Consequently, it appears that neither through the traditional device of stockownership nor through that of bank loans can the major owners of capital exercise control over managerial decision making. So the claim that managers and technicians have wrested control of the private corporation from the major owners of capital appears quite well supported by the evidence. Presumably, analogous arguments could be used to show how manager-technicians have assumed control over every major institution in American society, including the federal government. (Think of the role of technicians like Henry Kissinger in shaping foreign policy with presidents as their mouthpieces.)

Technological Rationality

Suppose it is true that manager-technicians have wrested power over the large American corporation from the owners of capital, and hence that the large American corporation has been transformed from a capitalist institution to a technocratic institution. How does this help the Utopian's case? How does this provide evidence for the claim that postindustrial technological growth is bringing about proportionate decreases in scarcity, and ultimately will lead to the elimination of scarcity? We saw how the capitalist corporate system has consistently raised roadblocks to the elimination of scarcity. What makes the Utopian think that the technocratic firm will not do the same? The answer seems straightforward enough: the goals of the technocratic corporation will not conflict with attempts to eliminate scarcity, as the goals of the capitalist corporation did. In terms of its goals (such as the maximization of private profit), the capitalist corporation presupposed and stimulated scarcity; in terms of its goals, the technocratic corporation is militantly committed to ending scarcity.

But what makes the Utopian think that the goals of the technocratic corporation are any different from those of the capitalist corporation? Isn't the manager-technician, like the capitalist of old, primarily interested in making a profit? Why should a change in corporate leadership entail a change in goals? Here unfortunately no adequate answer is forthcoming from the theorists of the technocratic corporation. They have made a very persuasive case in defense of the claim that manager-technicians have taken over the large corporation, but their case in defense of the claim that the corporate goal-structure has correspondingly changed is very weak. For example, one Utopian, in speaking about corporate behavior, tells us

> From one point of view, this behavior can be termed "responsible": there is no display of greed or graspiness; there is no attempt to push off onto the workers or the community at large part of the social costs of the enterprise. *The modern corporation is a soulful corporation.*[9]

But the author nowhere tells us precisely what goals now make the corporation "soulful," and never really shows that it has these goals.

Getting very little help from the literature on the technocratic corporation, we can only try to figure out on our own whether a shift from capitalist to technocratic control would involve a shift in goals. There is good reason for thinking that it would.

That one group has wrested power from another group does not entail, by itself, any shift in values guiding key authoritative decisions. However, the emergence of the technocratic corporation involves not only a change in the groups which exercise power, but also in the instruments which provide the basis for such power; not only do technicians supplant capitalists in positions of power, but also technical expertise supplants the ownership of capital as the primary source of power. There are only a limited number of ways in which an instrument of power may be used to enhance and maintain one's power. By imposing limits on the way in which power may be exerted, the instrument may be thought to impose a set of goals on the key decisions which are effectively carried out by its use. It is obvious, in contexts where the private ownership of capital was the key to corporate control, that not every type of goal or activity could be pursued compatibly with the maintenance or enlargement of one's corporate power. People who hoarded their capital funds, or who diffused their ownership in many corporations, or who did not seek profits in the corporations they owned, would have little power or would fail to maintain or enhance the power they did have within the corporate system. Indeed, major owners of capital could maintain their power within the framework of the corporate system only if the corporations they owned had as their primary and overriding goal the maximization of profits. Thus, there is a whole system of goals associated with the capitalist control of the corporation which is rooted in the maximization of profits and which guides the formation of all major corporate plans and policies. From this, it is tempting to conclude that technical expertise, once it has begun to function as the primary instrument of corporate power, also generates a set of corporate goals with which it is uniquely correlated in the same way that private ownership of capital did when it functioned as the primary instrument of corporate control. Thus, as ownership control in the modern corporation is associated with market, or capitalist, rationality, so is managerial control, it is thought, associated with technological rationality.

We know what ultimate goals were foisted upon the capitalist by capital ownership as an instrument of power: the maximization of profits and personal wealth. But what ultimate goals are foisted upon the manager-technician by technical expertise as an instrument of power? The answer seems surprisingly simple. If technical expertise is the source of power, then manager-technicians can only maintain and expand their power, both as individuals and as a group, by stimulating both the growth and applications of technological knowledge. The more knowledge, the more power; the greater the application of that knowledge, the more power. Thus it appears the ultimate goal of the technocratic corporation is maximal growth in technology. But the pursuit of technological growth expresses itself as the pursuit of increasing mastery over nature, which in turn is achieved in part through increasing efficiency; that is, the increasing ability to get more and more out of less and less. Hence, insofar as technological growth is an ultimate goal of the technocratic corporation, then so is increasing mastery over nature, and increasing efficiency. And, insofar as technological growth presupposes scientific growth and economic growth, then scientific growth and economic growth are subsidiary goals of the technocratic corporation.

Furthermore, the increased application of technological knowledge presupposes the increased application of certain procedural goals in the production process. Every phase of the productive processes, or other institutional processes, should be increasingly subject to careful analysis, planning, and precise calculation. All decisions and procedures should be increasingly governed by impersonal, standardized, and explicitly formalized criteria; the work force should be inceasingly distributed in terms of precisely defined functions and specializations. There should be a increasingly strong tendency to routinize and atomize these functions, and then to integrate them within a well-defined and formalized organizational structure. Wherever possible, functions that can be performed by human beings should be mechanized and automated; that is, as much as is possible, humans should be replaced by machines. Humans should be increasingly characterized and evaluated in terms of their abilities to carry out functions and roles which contribute to the objectives of the institution. An institution which was not technologically rational in these senses (which did not pursue technocratic goals) would for example exhibit some of the following characteristics: its decisions would be based on supernatural belief, magic, poetic insight, or tradition; it would carry out its practices spontaneously, or on the basis of habit, tradition, or cult; human interactions would be personalized and informal; efficiency would be set aside whenever it conflicted with folk values or religious taboos.

Thus, we have a set of goals which, it appears, a technocratic firm would hold as primary; that is, it would pursue them at the expense of other goals. These are goals which would have to be pursued by any group whose power derives from technical expertise, if that group wants to maintain that power. The partial list goes as follows:

Substantive Goals:
Technological growth
Growth in human control over nature
Growth in efficiency
Scientific growth
Economic growth (at least at this time)

Procedural Goals:
Increasing use of analysis, planning, and precise calculation
Increasing use of impersonal, standardized, and formalized criteria
Increasing use of precisely defined functions and, specializations
Increasing routinization and atomization of functions
Increasing integration of functions within a formalized organization
Increasing mechanization and automatization of jobs
Increasing evaluation of workers in terms of functions and roles

These are the goals which appear to constitute technological rationality, as opposed to market or capitalist rationality (maximization of profits and of personal wealth). The technocratic firm will subordinate profits and the wealth of its owners to these goals. If profit maximization is incompatible with building specialized science laboratories, frequently modernizing production equipment, maximizing corporate growth, and eliminating personal favoritism, then profits will not be maximized. (However, even in the technocratic firm, some minimal profits must be earned to finance future science laboratories, future modernized equipment, and future growth.) Similarly, the capitalist firm will pursue the goals of technological rationality only when it suits the maximization of profits; for example, new machinery will be introduced if it lowers production costs, or a new scientific idea will be bought if it considerably increases revenue. On the other hand, a capitalist firm will search for cheap labor abroad rather than increase worker productivity at home or will search for cheap resources abroad rather than improve its resource-extraction techniques at home if its profits are thereby enhanced; and it will abstain from producing superior goods if this would result in decreased sales (say, because the product lasts longer). The technocratic firm would behave otherwise.

Technocracy and Scarcity

Would the technocratic corporate system cope better with the problems of scarcity than the capitalist corporations did? There seems to be reason to believe that it would. Since technocrats are not involved in corporate activity primarily to maximize their wealth, the technocratic system can be expected to generate less inequality in income and less poverty. Furthermore, while technocrats are committed to a fully planned economy, successful economic planning is difficult to achieve in the face of mass discontent. It is easier to plan well if one can keep people happy. So there is an incentive for technocrats to attempt to eliminate poverty and other sources of popular discontent, if only to facilitate the planning process.

Technocratic systems could also be expected to deal effectively with pollution and other forms of environmental breakdown. Whereas the production of pollution often seems in accord with the goals of capitalism—generating pollution can be profitable—it also seems to be a blatant contradiction of the goals of technological rationality. As an unintended byproduct, pollution is an expression of humankind's still very incomplete mastery of nature. And the more pollution grows, the more it detracts from our control over nature; in the end, of course, pollution will destroy us all, and therewith any mastery of nature we may have achieved. But the mastery of nature is a fundamental goal of technocratic systems; hence, the elimination of pollution and other external diseconomies seems to be required by the goals of technocratic systems.

But can we expect technocratic systems to arrest the trend toward growing wants and needs? We cannot if these systems are committed to economic growth, which it appears they would need be for a while. But would they always be compelled to pursue economic growth? This is a difficult question to answer. If indeed there came a time when science and technology could continue to grow, and at the same time humankind's mastery over nature could continue to expand in the absence of economic growth, then it would no longer be necessary for technocratic systems to pursue economic growth. Whether or not this is possible will be discussed in more detail in later chapters (see chapters 7 and 10).

Conclusion

We asked what basis Utopians could have for believing that the postindustrial revolution in technology will lead to the elimination of scarcity. No Utopian I know of has given a systematic defense of this claim. What I did was to reconstruct a defense seemingly implied in the works of some important Utopians. It goes like this: to set the stage for the elimination of scarcity, postindustrial technology must put an end to those trends (such as toward poverty, pollution, and compulsive consumption) that counteract the scarcity-inducing effects of growing technology. It does this by replacing industrial technology and eliminating the capitalist corporate system, the chief sources of these counteracting trends. Postindustrial technology brings about the rise of a technocratic corporate system, and with it a technocratic government system which will ultimately eliminate poverty, greatly reduce the effects of pollution, and arrest compulsive consumption. So goes the argument. Though persuasive, it is open to serious criticism. What form this criticism will take is revealed in chapter 11, where the Socialist view of technology is introduced. The belief in the emergence of technocracy seems to me to be absolutely crucial to the Utopian argument. The Socialist critique of this belief will prove to be devastating.

Notes

[1] John Kenneth Galbraith, *The New Industrial State* (New York: New American Library, 1967), pp. 57–71.
[2] Ibid., pp. 23–45.
[3] Ibid., pp. 71–82.
[4] Ibid., pp. 92–93.
[5] Ibid., pp. 90–91.
[6] A. A. Berle and G. C. Means, *The Modern Corporation and Private Property* (New York: Macmillan, 1934), p. 115.

[7]Robert J. Larner, "Ownership and Control in the 200 Largest Nonfinancial Corporations, 1929 and 1963," in *American Economic Review*, 56, No. 4 (Sept. 1966), 777–787.

[8]Ibid. pp. 46–56, 91–92.

[9]Carl Kaysen, "The Social Significance of the Modern Corporation," in *American Economic Review*, 47, No. 2 (May 1957), 313–314. Emphasis added.

5

Scarcity and Aggression

A Catalog of Social Evils

We come now to the last, and most troublesome, premise of the Utopian argument, namely the claim that the elimination of scarcity will lead to the elimination of every major social evil. This extremely ambitious claim is very difficult to test. We have always lived in scarcity, and thus have no direct knowledge of what conditions would obtain were scarcity eliminated; we can only guess from meager evidence available to us.

Obviously, the issues raised by this claim are too vast for this one chapter. So I will focus somewhat by concentrating on one class of social evils, those that express human aggression (such as war, violent crime, and competition). I will ask whether there is evidence that aggression can be eliminated and whether its elimination is connected with the elimination of scarcity. There has been heated controversy on this of late, stimulated by the work of Konrad Lorenz and Robert Ardrey, among others. I will draw whatever conclusions can be drawn from the controversy. This is not to say, however, that I will neglect other major social evils. And indeed, in the chapters on the Dystopian view I will need to touch on many of them. Let me explain this further.

First, let me mention something about the nature of social evils. Not every human evil is a social evil. Stated simply, a social evil is any barrier to the happiness of all or a large number of individuals, and one that comes from, or is reinforced by, their social or natural environments. In other words, a social evil is an evil for which society is responsible or with which society could cope. For example, suppose Jones gets drunk habitually through his own fault, meaning that there are no social pressures, or socially induced personal tragedies, which lead him to do so. Suppose further than Jones's drunkenness causes no great harm to other people. Under such conditions, Jones's drunkenness is not a social evil, though it may well be an evil for Jones (his health is ruined, for example). If drunks were not numerous, and were all like Jones, then drunkenness would not be a social problem. (As a matter of fact, it is indeed a social evil: it is reinforced by social institutions, it is too widespread, and it causes serious social dislocations.)

Poverty is a paradigmatic case of a social evil. No doubt some people are poor through their own fault. Nonetheless, poverty seems to be the inevitable result of our social and natural environments. Ultimately, the social environment seems more responsible than the natural environment since it appears that society could eliminate the natural causes of poverty, or so the Utopians think. Society may not be to blame for each person who is poor, but it is to blame for the fact that there is the amount of poverty there is. (For some Utopians, such as B. F. Skinner, there are no human evils which are not social evils; according to them, our environment, and not ourselves, is ultimately to blame for all our miseries.)

Consider the following groupings of social evils:

Economic evils:
Poverty
Economic inequality
Compulsive consumption
Waste and inefficiency
Pollution
Resource depletion
Exploitation
Political-institutional evils:
Political coercion
Mass manipulation

Political inequality
Institutionalized racism, sexism, etc.
Inadequate mass participation
Curtailment of basic freedoms
Bureaucratic centralism
Corruption

Aggression-related evils:
War
Violent crime
Rioting
Sadism and brutality
Hatred
Untrammeled competition

Cultural-psychological evils:
Ignorance
Sexual repression
Mass apathy
Depersonalized human relations
Alienated work
Spreading neurosis, anxiety, insanity
Alienation from nature

This is only a working classification of social evils. It is not meant to be exhaustive. The lines of division are somewhat arbitrary, but it will do for the purposes of my analysis.

Utopians need not claim that all the items in the above list of social evils will be eliminated with the elimination of scarcity. For what is an evil now may no longer be an evil at the time postscarcity occurs. Once population growth was considered good; now it is apparently an evil. Conversely, economic inequality, now an evil, may no longer be an evil in a postscarcity society. If all people get what they need and want, then the existence of economic inequality (inequality in wealth and income) is merely an expression of the fact that some people need and want more than others. However, where everyone gets what he or she needs, there seems nothing wrong with some getting more because they need more. In contexts of scarcity, though, economic inequality seems definitely to be an evil (though perhaps a necessary one), for here it implies inequality of opportunity to satisfy one's needs, while in postscarcity it does not.

What Utopians are claiming, then, is the following: each "evil" in the above list will either be eliminated following the onset of postscarcity or will be transformed into a nonevil. This second possibility needs to be kept in mind. Some Utopians—especially Skinner—do incorporate in their model of an ideal technological society some of the "evils" listed above (such as political inequality and mass manipulation). Skinner argues strenuously that, in ideal conditions, these so-called evils will no longer be evils.

Socialists generally agree with Utopians that the elimination of scarcity is the key to the elimination or transformation of all major social evils listed above. Contrarily, Dystopians maintain that the movement toward a postscarcity society can only intensify, rather than eliminate, many of these social evils. The evils Dystopians think most likely to grow as technology grows and societies prosper are political-institutional evils and cultural-psychological evils. For this reason, I will delay the discussion of political-institutional and cultural-psychological evils, and their connection to the struggle against scarcity, until we reach part two and the chapters dealing with the Dystopian view (especially chapters 6–8).

Dystopians quite correctly admit that economic evils will disappear, or be transformed into nonevils, if scarcity is eliminated. These evils are merely manifestations of scarcity (such as poverty and pollution), as I have already argued, so nothing more need be said about them at this time. (Some Dystopians claim that technological growth will intensify the problem of scarcity, and hence economic evils. We will take up this issue in chapters 7 and 10.)

This leaves only, for the present, aggression-related evils. What is surprising is that many Dystopians concede that the elimination of scarcity will lead also to the elimination of aggression-related evils. Aldous Huxley, for one, allows that in the "Brave New World" (the future affluent technological society) war, violence, and crime will virtually be eliminated. Most other Dystopians simply neglect to discuss the aggression issue at all.

Nonetheless, the question of the elimination of aggression needs to be taken up. Most people think that aggression is an enduring feature of the human condition; they do not believe that war, crime, and violence will be significantly reduced by the elimination of scarcity. But this goes squarely against the Utopian view. Utopians clearly need to prove that human aggression can be eliminated and that the struggle against scarcity is the key to its elimination. They cannot, as

Buckminster Fuller and others often do, merely assume this to be the case. Equally clearly, the evils stemming from human aggression are among the most serious of social evils; Utopians must focus more on these than on most other kinds of evils. For the remainder of this chapter, I will discuss the issue of the elimination of human aggression; the other social evils will be taken up later. I will say less about technology here than elsewhere, but obviously the topic of aggression is central to the analysis of Utopian and other views on the social role of technology.

Aggression: Utopians versus Realists

To the Utopian view of human aggression, I oppose the "Realist" view. Whereas Utopians believe that human aggression can and will be eliminated, Realists believe that it cannot be eliminated. The ranks of the Realists include most people who have reflected on the human condition, the famous as well as the anonymous, the contemporary as well as the ancient. They include Plato, Aristotle, St. Augustine, Machiavelli, Thomas Hobbes, John Locke, John Stuart Mill, and Friedrich Nietzsche, as well as such twentieth-century writers as Robert Ardrey, Konrad Lorenz, and William F. Buckley, Jr.

Can Utopians prove their position about human aggression to be correct in the face of such opposition? I think not. The evidence from the life, behavioral, and social sciences is too meager to determine the veracity of the Utopian position, or, for that matter, the veracity of the Realist position. Utopians have one recourse, however. They can attempt to undermine the reasons usually given for the Realist view by showing that the arguments given for that view are bad ones. Although, unfortunately, no Utopians have succeeded in doing this, it can be done. In the remainder of this chapter, speaking for Utopians I will argue that the evidence usually given by Realists fails to support their position; if anything, the Realists' evidence supports the Utopian position, although it falls short of proving it.

History

In denying that the human propensity toward aggression can be eliminated, Realists initially seem to have the whole of history on their side.

After all, isn't the course of history replete with war, persecution, oppression, murder, rape, and theft? However, this apparently endless chronology of aggression and violence is not necessarily strong evidence for the Realist position. Supposing that humans have always been violent in the past, why should we expect them to continue to be so in the future? Why cannot the factors which have caused violence in the past be eradicated or greatly modified in the future? If there were no novelty in history, no asymmetry, no unidirectional change, then the Realist view would be eminently plausible. But, for a number of key phenomena which we have already noted (such as science, technology, and economic production), there obviously is systematic novelty and unidirectional growth. Of course, it may be that there is no novelty or change in those factors which have accounted for the past aggressive behavior of humans, but this cannot be taken for granted. So the whole accumulated history of human aggression counts in favor of the Realist position only if the factors generating past human aggression cannot be eliminated or subjected to major modification. Thus before we can determine whether or not the Realist position is plausible, we must find out which account of past human aggression is most reasonable.

If the factors accounting for the patterns of human behavior are classified as either environmental or genetic, then Realists seem committed to a genetic (or innatist) explanation, and Utopians to an environmentalist explanation, of the seemingly universal human propensity for aggression. For it seems that any environmental factor (such as weather patterns, educational systems, production processes) can in principle be eliminated or substantially modified. But aggression, according to Realists, will always be present no matter how the environment is transformed. Realists thus seem to believe that aggression springs from "human nature" (or, in the usual jargon, that it is "innate" to all humans). According to them, the universal human aggressive drive is transmitted genetically (inherited), rather than acquired (learned) through the pressures of the environment. On the other hand, Utopians think that humans will be able to rid themselves of this aggressive drive once they are able to isolate and control the environmental factors that reinforce it. For practical purposes we can assume that the disagreement between Utopians and Realists on the eliminability of aggression reduces to a disagreement between environmentalist and innatist accounts of its origins.

Once its essential commitment to innatism is revealed, the Realist position can no longer appear as plausible as it once did. Only a minority of humans in the past have engaged in acts of killing, fighting, or theft, and a number of these only did so in self-defense or in response to some order (as in war). (And the latter cannot be said *prima facie* to have acted aggressively or to have exhibited a basic drive toward aggression.) So unless they bring in striking new evidence, the best Realists can say is that a large minority of humans have a strong inherited tendency toward fighting and killing. This is certainly not enough to support their thesis, for as long as a large number of human beings are not innately aggressive, aggression can in principle be eliminated through selective breeding.

It is crucial for Realists therefore to establish that all or almost all humans are innately aggressive. But then they must explain away the fact that only a minority of humans have exhibited the sort of fighting behavior that springs from an aggressive drive. The most obvious countermove for Realists is to maintain that most humans fail to display sustained fighting behavior only because they are deterred from doing so by the state coercive apparatus (and, to a lesser degree, by other forms of socialization). If the coercive apparatus were eliminated, we are told, there would be "war of every man against every man," and life, as a consequence, would be "nasty, brutish, and short."[1] The evidence in favor of this thesis is usually culled from the behavior of nations with respect to one another (since they themselves are not under the effective control of any international coercive organization), as well as from the behavior of individuals within the context of social disorder and anarchy. But evidence of another sort is also needed: if indeed most people are deterred from directly carrying out their aggressive drives, then either they are considerably frustrated or they have found a peaceful outlet for their aggressiveness. Realists are thus compelled to reinterpret many forms of behavior not involving physical attack either as expressions of the frustration of aggressive impulses (kicking tires, pounding desks), as peaceful outlets for aggression (sports, business competition, debates), or as "symbolic" aggression (dreams about war and killing).

There is direct evidence against the claim that if not subject to political coercion all humans would tend to behave aggressively. Primitive hunting societies do not have armed police, bodyguards, or special armies. They do not have any state coercive apparatus; the power of chiefs and shamans rests on persuasion rather than coercion. The reasons for this are simple. The food-producing procedures in a hunting society are not efficient enough to be carried out by a specialized group; each person, including the chief and the shaman, spends a large amount of time in the hunt. Hence, there is little room for an effective division of labor or for the development of those occupational specialties essential to the administrative and coercive functions of the state. Though there may be periodic fighting, there is nothing like a war of every man against every man in hunting societies. And there is little prolonged warfare between hunting societies, a fact easily explained by the nomadic character of hunting societies, by the absence of specialized armies, and by the constant pressures of the search for food. Thus the existence of hunting societies seems to belie the claim of a human aggressive instinct.[2]

But suppose we grant the contention that up to now all humans have been strongly inclined to act aggressively. Are we thereby forced to embrace the Realists' innatist hypothesis about aggression, or can we formulate an environmentalist hypothesis which is more congenial to the Utopian position? Given the enormous variation in environments from time to time and place to place, we normally tend to account for variable forms of behavior by appealing to the changing environment, and to account for temporally and spatially invariant forms of behavior by appealing to universal mechanisms of inheritance. This perhaps accounts for our initial temptation to side with Realists rather than with Utopians. In this case, however, such a temptation should be resisted. For example, economic scarcity is one environmental factor invariably correlated with widespread human aggression. In every society where there has been aggression there has been scarcity. Thus Utopians can explain the constancy of human aggression through history by reference to the constancy of the scarcity environment through history. Obviously, much aggression is elicited by the competition for scarce goods (such as food, land, and gold) or for offices (such as kingship) giving one power over scarce goods. But there is much more to the connection between aggression and scarcity than this. The scarcity environment may also indirectly foster aggression insofar as it gives rise to institutions which reinforce aggressive tendencies. The function of many institutions is to enable people to cope more effectively with the problems of scarcity, and many of the essential characteristics of these institutions are determined by the way they carry out this function.

Some institutions (such as governments) authoritatively allocate and distribute scarce resources and goods; others (such as corporations) produce these goods; and still other institutions (such as the family and universities) train and socialize those who partake in production. It is obvious that those institutions whose major function is to prepare and mobilize human resources for the process of production, or to protect the interests of those getting the largest share of production, will behave in a repressive and frustrating way. If, as is believed, frustration induces aggression, then institutions coping with the problems of scarcity by imposing heavy burdens, insuperable obstacles, or grossly unequal distributions will by their behavior considerably strengthen the general tendency toward aggression. Furthermore, in addition to their repressive impact, the institutions having to cope with the problem of scarcity will also positively reinforce the sorts of attitudes and practices (such as competition, desire for power, desire for prestige, and patriotism) which strongly predispose their possessor toward aggression. In conclusion, the presence of economic scarcity can account for human aggression in two ways: it provides the motive for many acts of aggression, and it occasions the rise of institutions which, in their normal workings, create a considerable amount of aggression-inducing frustration and reinforce the sorts of character traits which, in the absence of deterrence, culminate in aggression.

That there is a positive correlation between economic scarcity and aggression was suggested quite forcefully by Robert MacNamara in 1966 in his well-known Montreal speech:

> At the beginning of 1958, there were twenty-three prolonged insurgencies going on about the world. As of February 1, 1966, there were forty.
>
> Further, the total number of outbreaks of violence has increased each year: in 1958, there were thirty-four; in 1965 there were fifty-eight.
>
> But what is most significant of all is that there is a direct and constant relationship between the incidence of violence and the economic status of the countries afflicted.
>
> The World Bank divides nations, on the basis of per capita income, into four categories: rich, middle-income, poor, and very poor.
>
> The rich nations are those with a per capita income of $750 per year or more. The current United States level is more than $2,700. There are twenty-seven of these rich nations. They possess 75 percent of the world's wealth, though roughly only 25 percent of the world's population.

Since 1958, only *one* of these twenty-seven nations has suffered a major internal upheaval on its own territory.

But observe what happens at the other end of the economic scale. Among the thirty-eight very poor nations—those with a per capita income of under $100 a year—no less than thirty-two have suffered significant conflicts. Indeed, they have suffered an average of two major outbreaks of violence per country in the eight-year period. That is a great deal of conflict.

What is worse, it has been, predominantly, conflict of a prolonged nature. The trend holds predictably constant in the case of the two other categories: the poor and the middle-income nations. Since 1958, 87 percent of the very poor nations, 69 percent of the poor nations, and 48 percent of the middle-income nations have suffered serious violence.

There can, then, be no question that there is an *irrefutable relationship between violence and economic backwardness.* And the trend of such violence is up, not down.[3]

Thus it appears that we can give either an innatist account of the history of constant human aggression, as the Realists do, or a wholly environmentalist account, as the Utopians do. Realists will appeal to a universally inherited aggressive drive and Utopians to a universally present scarcity environment to account for the constancy of aggression through history. Are the accounts deadlocked? Is one as good as the other? I think not; everything else being equal, the Utopian account is better than the Realist account if human history is the major source of evidence.

Realists initially must concede that the scarcity environment has always existed and has always been an important cause or reinforcer of human aggression. On the other hand, Utopians are not initially compelled to accept the existence of any universal instinct toward aggression; unlike the scarcity environment, an aggressive instinct is a theoretical entity whose existence initially has to be defended rather than conceded. Realists must subscribe to a two-factor theory of aggression, while Utopians need hold only to a one-factor theory; Realists must allow for the postulation of the scarcity environment as well as of an aggressive instinct as an important source of human aggression, while Utopians need initially postulate no more than the scarcity environment. By any standard of simplicity, the Utopian account of the origins of human aggression is simpler than the Realist account; everything else being equal, it is more rational to subscribe to the Utopian account than to the Realist account. The burden of proof is on Realists to show why the scarcity environment is inadequate to account for the history of all human aggression, and why further appeal must be made to an inherited drive. But this is impossible for Realists to do so long as they restrict themselves to the study of human history. To justify their claims, Realists would have to show that, were there not a universal human aggressive instinct, there would be considerably less aggression than is actually found in historical societies, and that, in the absence of a scarcity environment, humans would still exhibit a strong drive toward aggression. Unfortunately, as long as human history is our only source of evidence, neither assertion can be directly tested. Since, according to the Realists, humans have always been instinctively aggressive, there is no way to find out by the study of history how humans would have behaved had they not had such an instinct. Again, since economic scarcity has always existed and has always had a considerable influence on human behavior, there is no way of telling directly what human behavior would have been like in the absence of human scarcity. Given the historical facts at their disposal, the Realists have no appeal other than to our intuitions; they can only make us "feel" that the environment cannot by itself explain our aggressive urges or the widespread fighting in and between human societies. As long as we focus exclusively on human history there is no way in which Realists can justify our accepting their two-factor theory (instinct and environment) rather than some one-factor theory (such as the scarcity environment) of human aggression. Given our present state of historical knowlege, the Utopian account is preferable to the Realist account because it is simpler.

We began with the widespread opinion that the facts of history are overwhelmingly on the side of the Realist view. But our analysis has shown that, as long as only the facts of history are considered, the Realist innatist view turns out to be less reasonable than the Utopian or other environmentalist views. As long as we restrict our attention to human history, the Realist view must appear to be wholly gratuitous. We are thus led to the very surprising conclusion that the Realist view can be shown to be more plausible than the Utopian or other environmentalist views only when we go beyond the study of human history. In the following sections, we shall look at recent evidence which has breathed new life into the Realist view.

Human Behavior at Birth

Realists obviously cannot defend their hypothesis successfully as long as they restrict themselves to the study of human behavior under the influence of the scarcity environment. They are thus compelled to seek out evidence either from the study of animals or newly born humans, since all socialized humans have been affected directly or indirectly by the scarcity environment. The second course of action (the observation of human infant behavior) is hardly promising because of the small temporal period within which the behavior of the human infant can be examined before the onset of socialization. Specifically, within the period after birth it is extremely difficult to distinguish between an unconditioned or unlearned response, on the one hand, and a truly instinctive response, on the other. When watching a newborn child we note all sorts of behaviors which seem unconditioned or unlearned, such as crying when wet or when hungry. It would be a mistake to conclude from this, however, that humans have a crying instinct. That a sequence of behavior is instinctive entails not only that it is originally unlearned, but also that it cannot later be extinguished through learning, conditioned out, or forgotten. It is possible for an organism to learn to refrain from performing an unconditioned reflex which it exhibited at birth; a child can be taught to verbalize demands rather than to cry. Basenji hounds are born aggressive and cocker spaniels docile, but basenji hounds can be trained to be docile, and cocker spaniels to be aggressive.[4] In these circumstances it would certainly be misleading, if not wrong, to say that basenji hounds are instinctively aggressive. If indeed the child's crying tendency and the basenji hound's aggressive tendency disappeared as a consequence of physical maturation rather than learning or forgetting, then they might be deemed to be instinctive. But this sort of instinct would be of no use to the Realist, since it does not find expression in adult life.

It should be obvious that the unconditioned responses exhibited at birth are not necessarily instinctive responses in any relevant sense. Conversely, there is no reason why all instinctive behavior has to be exhibited at birth. Some instinctive activity may appear only after the nervous system is sufficiently mature to support it. Some organisms can be said to instinctively know how to fly, swim, sing, or mate. It only means that they acquire this ability and this tendency simply as a consequence of the normal maturation of their physical organs, with no dependence on learning or experience. Experiments show that a bird, separated from its parents since birth and placed in a container which allows for no relevant practice or experience, will "know" how to fly at the appropriate time.[5]

Consequently, there is no necessary connection between instinctive behavior and behavior exhibited at birth. So the study of newly born humans does not provide one with the basis for distinguishing between behavior patterns which are instinctive and those which are not. It would be of little help to the Realist if humans were found to be mean and quarrelsome at birth, and it would do little damage to him or her if humans were found to be gentle and affectionate at birth. For any given species one cannot determine whether a behavior sequence is instinctive without examining the whole life of the individuals of that species under well-controlled experimental conditions. Specifically, one must be in a position to determine whether that behavior sequence emerges and is maintained even when the organism is deprived of the relevant stimulation, teaching, and experience for the learning of that sequence. Clearly, such deprivation experiments cannot be conducted with humans on a sufficiently large scale to be meaningful. In order to establish an aggressive instinct in men Realists must turn to the study of animals. Realists are thereby forced to follow a rather circuitous route. First, they must establish that some relevant species of animals are instinctively aggressive, and then, either by induction, analogy, or appeal to some already established theory, they must make the inference from the existence of an aggressive instinct in these animal species to the existence of a corresponding aggressive instinct in humans. This strategy, as is well known, is fraught with traps and obstacles. And so the Realist position which at first looked so safe begins to look quite risky. In the next section, I shall evaluate the Realist arguments which are based on the recent work in comparative psychology or ethology.

Evolution and Animal Behavior

Much of the recent evidence for an aggressive instinct in humans emanates from the work of European ethologists such as Nickolaas Tinbergen, Konrad Lorenz, and W. H. Thorpe, and has been popularized in Robert Ardrey's *African Genesis* and Lorenz's *On Aggression*.[6] In contrast with their counterpart American animal psychologists, European ethologists typically study the behavior of animals in the wild rather than in sophisticated laboratories. They are more interested in discovering the natural patterns of behavior peculiar to various species than in seeing how the behavior patterns of that species can be modified by experimental manipulation and conditioning. This approach of course does accentuate and facilitate the discovery of instinctive behavior patterns in animals. And these workers have argued persuasively for the existence of intraspecific aggressive instincts in many species of vertebrates, but especially in fishes and birds. That is, they have attempted to show that many vertebrates have an instinctive tendency to commit acts of aggression against each other. This no one contends with. What has invited opposition and recrimination has been the attempt by Ardrey and Lorenz to extend these conclusions to human beings; that is, most of the controversy stems from Ardrey's and Lorenz's attempts to use these discoveries of aggressive instincts in animals to establish the existence of a counterpart aggressive instinct in man.

How do Ardrey and Lorenz argue from the existence of an aggressive instinct in many species of animals to an aggressive instinct in humans? They don't merely say, "Well, many kinds of animal are instinctively aggressive; therefore, humans must also be instinctively aggressive." That would be silly. Rather than arguing inductively (by listing all the species which have been found to be innately aggressive), they argue theoretically, somewhat as follows. Animal species are instinctively aggressive because aggression is useful for species survival. Thus we can assume that human aggressive behavior contributes to the survivability of the human species. We can further conclude that aggression, as a species-surviving trait of humans, is transmitted genetically from parents to children.

What are the species-adaptive functions of aggression in animals? Though they have attributed many such functions to aggression, such as selective mating and the establishment of a social dominance structure, Lorenz and others have placed primary emphasis on the crucial role of aggression in enabling communities within a species to establish and maintain certain territories for their exclusive use. It is the "territorial imperative" which according to them primarily warrants the aggressive instinct.[7] Territoriality, in turn, is thought to be highly adaptive because of its contributions to

> the maintenance of dispersion, so that individual hunting techniques may be performed without interference; the maintenance of an area providing for a food supply requisite for rearing young or maintaining group existence; the reduction of crowding of cryptic nests so as to reduce the likelihood of their discovery by predators; and the prevention of interference with nesting, courtship, mating, and sometimes the rearing of the young.[8]

This theoretical evolutionary argument in defense of the thesis that humans are instinctively aggressive may have initial appeal. But ultimately it fails to work for fairly straightforward reasons. To appreciate this, we need to schematize the argument more rigorously, as follows:

1. Species whose members establish and hold territories have a decided evolutionary selective advantage over species whose members do not
2. Consequently, it is highly probable that the members of successfully adapted species will exhibit territorial behavior
3. Territoriality is achieved most effectively through intraspecific aggression (aggression against members of one's species)
4. Consequently, it is highly probable that the members of successfully adapted species will exhibit intraspecific aggressive behavior
5. Therefore, it is highly probable that the members of successfully adapted species are instinctively aggressive; that is, they will have an inherited tendency toward aggression against members of the species
6. Consequently, since the human species has evolved under the pressures of natural selection, and has adapted successfully, it is highly probable that its members are instinctively aggressive.

This argument has a number of serious faults. For one thing, it assumes what is manifestly false—that territoriality and aggression are universally and absolutely adaptive. But no trait is universally or absolutely adaptive; it is adaptive only relative to a set of functions which may be necessary for the survival of some species but disruptive for the survival of others. For example, barking and the propensity to chew on bones are adaptive for dogs but not for chickens. And surely the functions associated with territoriality, such as dispersion and the reduction of crowding of nests, do not apply to all species. Furthermore, even for those contexts in which a given trait is adaptive, it confers a selective advantage on those species which possess it only if everything else is equal. But generally everything else is not equal; a species which lacks a specific adaptive trait will generally exhibit mechanisms or characteristics which compensate for the lack of that trait. Some species (such as insects) may compensate for their lack of territoriality and hence lessened ability to protect their brood by reproducing at a much higher rate than others. Othe species (such as primates) may achieve widespread spacing over their ecological niche through the processes of foraging and roaming rather than through the holding of specific territories.[9]

Just as the holding of territories is not necessary for (though it contributes to) adequate spacing and the survival of an adequate number of the young, neither is aggression necessary for (though it contributes to) the successful holding of territories by small communities. Any device which signals ownership and elicits withdrawal by a transient of one's species (such as posture, odor, territorial marking, and ritualized threat displays) will do just as well as aggression.[10] In fact, many kinds of animals are able to maintain their territory against the claims of members of their species with hardly any resort to fighting, other than "sham" fighting. It should also be emphasized that aggression as a technique for the holding of territories has serious disadvantages not shared by alternative techniques, such as widespread injury and serious demands on the defender's attention and energy. Therefore, there is simply no basis for saying that aggression confers upon all species who display it a selective advantage over the species who do not and, hence, there is no basis for saying that all species which adapt in the long run will generally display aggressive behavior.

Even if it were conceded that territoriality and aggression were universally adaptive for all vertebrate species—including humans "in the wild"—and therefore that the members of all vertebrate species living "in the wild" tended to behave aggressively, the evolutionary argument for an innate aggressive drive in humans still would not work. From the fact that aggression was universally present in all vertebrate species living "in the wild," it would not follow that it was universally inherited by the members of these species. True, in some contexts it would be rational to infer from the universal presence of an adaptive trait in a species that it is inherited by all the members of that species. For example, this inference is valid for species in the lower reaches of the phylogenetic scale (such as insects, shellfish, and reptiles); here, adaptive traits (like knowing what foods to eat, how to get them, how to protect oneself, and how to build one's nests) are most easily passed on to all members through the mechanisms of heredity. However, the higher the species is in the phylogenetic scale (such as are cats and monkeys) the less reasonable is it to assume, in the absence of further evidence, that an adaptive trait generally or universally displayed by members of a species (for instance, eating bananas and using tools) is universally inherited by members of that species (such as the chimpanzee). For the higher one moves up the phylogenetic scale, the more adaptive it is for species to acquire desirable behavioral traits through learning rather than through inheritance. For those species having a sufficiently large brain to store memories, a low reproductive rate, and a comparatively long period of maturation learning is more adaptive than instinct. The only way such species can adapt with sufficient rapidity to significant long-term changes in the environment is through the capacity to learn from their individual members. Thus in the upper reaches of the phylogenetic scale, those species whose universally displayed adaptive traits are learned through universal training procedures have a selective advantage, everything else being equal, over those species whose universally displayed adaptive traits are instinctive. So the evolutionary argument purporting to establish an aggressive instinct in humans turns against itself. If it were able to establish (which it cannot) that all species exhibit a general tendency toward aggression, the argument would lead us to the complementary conclusions that species in the middle and lower sectors of the phylogenetic scale (such as nonmammals) are instinctively aggressive and that species in the upper sectors of the phylogenetic scale (such as primates) have a universally learned propensity toward aggression, just as they may have a universally learned propensity to eat certain foods in certain prescribed ways. If the evolutionary argument worked, it would tend to support the environmentalist rather than innatist theory of human aggression; but, of course, it does not work.

In summary, the evolutionary argument suggested by Lorenz and others to show that humans are innately or instinctively aggressive fails for many reasons. Territoriality is not, as this argument assumes, absolutely adaptive for all species; aggression is not for all species the most effective way of maintaining territoriality; and finally, for higher species, the universal presence of an adaptive trait does not entail its instinctiveness or universal inheritance. Indeed, evolutionary theory suggests to the contrary that in humans and other higher species adaptive traits will tend to be learned rather than inherited. Everything else being equal, it is more adaptive for humans and other higher species to acquire complex adaptive traits through learning rather than through genetic transmission.

Aggression as an Aversive Drive

Suppose that, contrary to what I have shown, the view that human aggression is instinctive or innate had been successfully justified and had been universally accepted. Would the Realist position as a consequence be decidedly proved, and the Utopian position decidedly refuted? I think not. The following analysis will reveal that in its more plausible versions the innatist theory of human aggression is not strong enough to entail the truth of the Realist position and the falsity of the Utopian position.

Realists say that human aggression cannot be eliminated in a nonfrustrative way through human effort and planning; Utopians obviously disagree. But if Utopians were forced to concede that human aggression indeed is genetically transmitted, how could they deal with the Realist position? They would have two options. The first would be to abandon the environmentalist stance and to pin their hopes totally on future prospects for genetic engineering. They could argue that, with future developments in biological technology, the distinction between nature and nurture and between heredity and environment would no longer be practically significant. To put it crudely: if humans, as we know them, are born aggressive, then one alternative may be to try to produce a new kind of nonaggressive human being by changing the gene structures transmitted from human to human.

Happily, Utopians would not have to resort to such a far out rejoinder, even if they were forced to accept the view that aggression is instinctive. Rather, they could maintain that a behavior pattern's being instinctive is perfectly compatible with its being eliminable through environmental manipulation. They could make the following argument.

First, let us distinguish between two kinds of instinctive drives: *appetitive* and *nonappetitive*.[11] To appreciate this distinction, we first must remind ourselves that no instinctive drive is "activated" at all times; in other words, no one ever inherits a propensity to perform a kind of behavior in all circumstances. What one inherits is a tendency to want something, or to do something, under certain circumstances. These circumstances may be internal or external to the organism. Where the circumstances are internal, the organism will have inherited a propensity to do or to want to do a kind of behavior when its internal physiology either becomes unstabilized or loses equilibrium. As an example, though the desire to eat is an inherited desire, it is activated only when the organism is in need of certain nutrients; an organism is not always hungry. Similarly, it does not always desire sex even though the desire for sex is inherited. Being hungry or intensely desiring sex seems associated with a condition of disequilibrium or instability within the organism; the consumption of food and the achievement of orgasm seem associated with the reassertion of the former internal condition of equilibrium. When this happens, the inherited hunger drive and sex drive is "deactivated."

Hunger and sex are examples of inherited appetitive drives. The wants and behavior associated with appetitive drives are functions of cyclical changes in the organism's internal physiology. Search or appetition (involving the activation of the drive) is followed by consumption, which in turn is followed by satiation (the deactivation of the drive); search or appetition is associated with the breakdown of hormonal or metabolic balances (the activation of the drive), and satiation (the deactivation) with the readjustment of these balances. It is to appetitive drives that Sigmund Freud's "hydraulic model" most adequately applies; one thinks of an original level of drive energy which continually builds up until it is released either spontaneously or by the appropriate stimulus-object (such as food or a willing sexual partner).

If one thinks of all instinctive drives as appetitive drives, then it will seem impossible to deactivate or eliminate any instinctive drive by the manipulation of the external environment; the cycle of activation and deactivation of aggressive drives is dependent primarily on internal physiology and not on the external environment. Indeed, Lorenz and others seem to view aggression as an instinctive appetitive drive.

But all this is wrong; not all instinctive drives are appetitive. For their activation some instinctive drives are primarily dependent on changes in their external environment, rather than on cyclical bodily changes. For example, the turkey hen has the inherited propensity to care for her chicks. She will typically accept as her chick any object which makes the characteristic cheeping call. On the other hand, if she is deafened she will exhibit no tendency toward maternal behavior; in fact, she will kill her chicks rather than care for them.[12] It is obvious that the turkey hen's maternal behavior, though instinctive, can be eliminated in a nonfrustrative way by the manipulation of a single auditory stimulus-variable.

Perhaps the most widespread form of nonappetitive instinctive drive is the "aversive drive"; an aversive drive is activated by, and elicits an appropriate response to, some threatening stimulus. Many ground-nesting birds (such as geese, ducks, turkeys, and pheasants) give alarm calls and crouch when a bird of prey passes over.[13] Again, the tendency to exhibit this alarm response to, for example, hawk-like stimuli is universally inherited rather than learned. The response can be nonfrustratively eliminated if the threatening stimulus is eliminated. Indeed, in this case it would be incongruous to look upon this sort of response as appetitive. It would be silly to think of these animals as cyclically building up a need to express the alarm response independently of the presence of any birds of prey and as being frustrated if no birds of prey show up over a long period to elicit the response. In this respect the inherited tendency to respond is radically different from the instinctive tendency to search for and consume food.

If territorial aggression were a selectively functional instinctive drive, then it would most rationally be construed as an aversive rather than an appetitive drive. Obviously, aggression is functional only to the extent that it occurs in response to appropriate threatening stimuli. If it were to appear cyclically, independent of events in the external environment, it would be a hindrance rather than an aid to individual and species survival. An aggressive drive which regularly began to build up until it found an outlet in behavior independent of the presence of appropriate stimuli would not only cause havoc and destruction within territorial communities but would also detract from the primary activities of the aggressive organism, such as the search for food and the building of domiciles. Aggression as an appetitive drive is a luxury which could only be afforded by organisms with a good deal of leisure time. And, indeed, where its existence is well confirmed, instinctive territorial aggressivness is a stimulus-bound aversive drive. The stickleback fish responds aggressively only to an intruder with a red underside; rats will resort to internal fighting within the community in response to high population stress. If we take seriously the Realists' evolutionary arguments, then we must conclude that the aggressive instinct (if it existed) would be aversive rather than appetitive. But if the aggressive instinct were aversive, aggressive drives could be permanently deactivated and aggressive behavior permanently eliminated in a nonfrustrative way by the elimination of all environmental aggression-inducing stimuli. For example, the propensity to make war could be deactivated even though it is inherited if all the environmental conditions which lead to war, such as fear-inducing and insecurity-inducing stimuli, were eliminated.

But suppose that, against all odds, Realists succeeded in establishing the innateness of aggression as an appetitive drive. Utopians could still hold onto their position though they would have to expand this concept of the environment to include the internal environment of the organism. But this may not be an important concession, since the internal environment in some cases may be easier to control than the external environment. Genes do not act on behavior directly, but rather through the intermediaries of tissues, organs, hormones, neural transmitters, enzymes, and the like. A set of genes might generate an appetitive aggressive drive by providing the instructions for the release of a large amount of some hormone (such as testosterone) or acid (for example, uric acid). Without genetic engineering, those with such a high appetitive propensity toward aggression could be treated, though not cured, in a manner not unlike that in which persons with genetic diseases are treated. Many genetic diseases are due to the tendency of the body to secrete or to accumulate an excessive amount of a certain substance (such as an enzyme, an acid, a mineral).[14] The usual procedure is either to inhibit the production of this substance or to eliminate or neutralize it. Presumably the excess hormone or acid which caused appetitive aggression could be subject to the same kind of treatment, such as the dispensation of "antiaggression" pills.

Conclusion

In this chapter I have begun the analysis of the last, and most ambitious, premise of the Utopian argument: that the elimination of scarcity will lead to the elimination of every major social evil. This premise is very difficult to assess since there are countless social evils. I have so far concentrated on aggression-related evils, leaving other evils (such as the curtailment of basic freedoms, mass manipulation, sexual repression, and alienated work) to be discussed in later chapters.

I analyzed in some detail the controversy between Utopians and Realists on the possibility for elimination of human aggression. Utopians, being environmentalists, think that human aggression can be eliminated once scarcity is eliminated; Realists, being innatists, think that human aggression can never be eliminated. I argued on the side of the Utopians and against the Realists. I did not attempt to prove the correctness of the Utopian position; I would not have known where to begin. But I did what appeared second best; I attempted to show that the arguments usually presented for the Realist position are bad arguments.

First, I attacked the historical and evolutionary reasons for thinking that human aggression is instinctive. I showed that one can more easily and simply give an environmentalist than an innatist explanation for the history of human aggression. I further showed that the evolutionary arguments are invalid at practically every step. Second, I argued that even if human aggression were instinctive, it would not follow that the alleged instinctive aggressive drive could not be deactivated by manipulation of the human internal and external environments. The claim that aggression is innate is perfectly compatible with the claim that aggressive behavior can be eradicated as a consequence of transformations in the human environment.

A Look Ahead

In part one I reconstructed what I thought to be the best Utopian argument. This argument consists of the premises that advanced societies are undergoing a postindustrial revolution in technology, that technology will continue to grow systematically in the postindustrial era, that postindustrial technological growth will lead eventually to the elimination of scarcity, and that the elimination of scarcity will lead to the elimination of every major social evil. I examined each of these premises and showed what assumptions underlie each of them. The first two premises were fairly easily acceptable, but the last two premises proved to be much more ambitious and controversial.

I presented the Utopian view as sympathetically as I could in order to neutralize somewhat the anti-Utopian biases which prevail nowadays, for we can never see our way clearly through the issues concerning the social role of technology if we let ourselves be swept along by the current fad without resistance. I have not, of course, been able to give a full defense of the Utopian view. It ultimately turns out to be dead wrong, as the chapters on the Dystopian and Socialist views will bear out. Nonetheless, it is important to see why technological Utopianism is attractive if we want to appreciate fully why it ultimately goes wrong. And a sympathetic discussion of the Utopian view forces us to look more carefully at a number of important topics, such as the nature of technology, technological growth, postindustrial technology, control over the corporation, the connection of knowledge and power, the values of technology (technological rationality), and the historical and evolutionary base of aggression. This we have done. We can now proceed to an examination of the Dystopian view.

Notes

[1]Thomas Hobbes, *Leviathan* (London: Oxford University Press, 1909), chapter 13.

[2]Gerhard Lenski, *Power and Privilege* (New York: McGraw-Hill, 1966), pp. 105–108; Robert K. Dentan, *Semai: A Nonviolent People of Malaya* (New York: Harper & Row, 1968).

[3]Seymour Melman, *Pentagon Capitalism* (New York: McGraw-Hill, 1970), pp. 158–160.

[4]Alexander Alland, Jr., *Evolution and Human Behavior* (Garden City: Natural History Press, 1967), pp. 132–134.

[5]Aubrey Manning, *An Introduction to Animal Behavior* (Reading, Mass.: Addison-Wesley, 1967), pp. 24–28.

[6]Konrad Lorenz, *On Aggression* (New York: Bantam, 1966), pp. 20–46; Robert Ardrey, *African Genesis* (New York: Atheneum, 1961).

[7]Lorenz, ibid.

[8]John Hurrell Crook, "The Nature and Function of Territorial Aggression" in M. F.

Ashley Montagu, ed., *Man and Aggression* (London: Oxford University Press, 1968), p. 164.

[9]Ibid., pp. 167–170.

[10]S. D. Barnett, "On the Hazards of Analogies" in Montagu, ed., *Man and Aggression*, p. 21.

[11]Crook, "Nature and Function of Aggression," p. 151.

[12]Konrad Lorenz, *Evolution and Modification of Behavior* (Chicago: University of Chicago Press, 1965), pp. 36–37.

[13]Manning, *Introduction to Animal Behavior*, pp. 51–52.

[14]Victor McKusick, *Human Genetics* (Englewood Cliffs, N.J.: Prentice-Hall, 1969), pp. 186–189.

Part Two

THE DYSTOPIAN VIEW

6

The Brave New World Reconsidered

Introduction

The Dystopian view is currently enjoying much better public reception than the Utopian view and for this reason I shall be more critical of the former than I was of the latter. This should help balance things off.

Dystopians say that continued technological growth is bringing about, and will continue to bring about, more harm than good. They place the blame for most of our major social problems on the needs and impact of modern technology.

Dystopians and Utopians stand at the opposite ends of the spectrum of views about the social worth of technology. Yet Dystopians are surprisingly in agreement with Utopians on many crucial points. Dystopians are in particular willing to accept many of the premises and assumptions of the Utopian argument which I analyzed in part one. They either agree or are willing to concede that advanced technological societies are moving into a postindustrial age in technology, and that in this age technology will continue a sustained growth, perhaps even at a more rapid pace. Many Dystopians, though not all, agree that continued technological growth will lead to the elimination of economic scarcity. And some, like many Utopians, think that technocratic power systems are gradually subverting and replacing capitalist and socialist power systems. What Dystopians almost universally reject in the Utopian argument is the premise that the elimination of scarcity will lead to the elimination of every major social evil. Contrary to this, they argue that the struggle against scarcity through continued technological growth can only exacerbate some of the more frightening social evils. These alleged technologically induced evils will be discussed in this and the following chapters.

I distinguish between two kinds of Dystopian criticism of modern technology: Classical Dystopian criticism and Countercultural Dystopian criticism. In this chapter I shall deal with the former, and in the remainder of part two, the latter.

The Classical criticisms are more typical of such earlier Dystopians as Fedor Dostoevski, Aldous Huxley, and George Orwell, though they have also found more recent expression in the work of Jacques Ellul. The classical criticisms have come mainly, though not exclusively, from men of letters, members of the clergy, and humanities professors. The Countercultural criticisms are more typical of recent spokesmen of the countercultural or "hip" youth movement of the 1960s and early 1970s, such as Herbert Marcuse, Theodore Roszak, Philip Slater, and Charles Reich.[1]

Classical Dystopian critics of modern technology accentuate its undesirable political repercussions, while Countercultural critics accentuate its undesirable psychological and cultural repercussions. Classical Dystopians blame the presumed decline or demise of political freedom, equality, and individualism on the imperatives of modern technology; Countercultural Dystopians blame the presumed growth of psychological alienation on the imperatives of modern technology.

I shall now move on to an examination of the Classical Dystopian criticisms. They revolve around the idea that modern technological growth is leading to the rise of dictatorial regimes with unprecedented powers of control and repression. The most popular model of this is presented in Aldous Huxley's *Brave New World*.

The Brave New World

Aldous Huxley's *Brave New World* is, in essence, a macabre fairy tale. Yet it is one of the most influential pieces of political literature of this century. It has been widely read, and those who have not read it seem to have absorbed its ideas by osmosis.

Huxley and many Dystopians since have warned that our modern technological societies are slowly drifting in the direction of a "Brave New World." Modern societies, we are told, are gradually being transformed into Brave New World societies, that is, societies very similar to that described so vividly by Huxley in his *Brave New World*. Twenty-seven years after the publication of that work, Huxley announced in retrospect:

> In 1931, when *Brave New World* was being written, I was convinced that there was plenty of time. The completely organized society, the scientific caste system, the abolition of free will by methodical conditioning, the servitude made acceptable by regular doses of chemically induced happiness, the orthodoxies drummed in by nightly courses of sleep-teaching— these events were coming all right, but not in my time, not even the time of my grandchildren. . . . Twenty-seven years later, in this third quarter of the twentieth century A.D. . . . I feel a good deal less optimistic than I did when I was writing *Brave New World*. The prophesies made in 1931 are coming much sooner than I thought they would. . . . The nightmare of total organization, which I had situated in the seventh century After Ford, has emerged from the safe, remote future and is now awaiting us, just around the next corner.[2]

Themes of this sort have been forcefully taken up recently by Jacques Ellul in his *Technological Society,* Herbert Marcuse in his *One Dimensional Man,* and Robert Heilbroner in his *Inquiry into the Human Prospect;* in the none-too-distant past, they were taken up by George Orwell in *1984* and Eugene Zamiatin in *We*.

This literature rarely fails to evoke a sympathetic response in us. We are apalled by the idea of a Brave New World. We do not want to lose our freedoms and nonconformist predilections. We do not want to be turned into moronic robots; nor do we want to be subject to constant manipulation and intrusion. The brainwashing techniques of Russian despots, the mass propaganda tools of fascist dictators, and even the antics of American presidents and their aides have made us glaringly aware that Brave New World stories are not wholly fairy tales.

Yet I fear that our completely negative response to the idea of a Brave New World is somewhat confused. We would have some difficulty proving what our intuitions tell us is true, namely, that Brave New World societies are very bad societies to live in. We would have some difficulty arguing against some of the moderate defenders of these societies, such as B. F. Skinner in his best-sellers *Walden Two* and *Beyond Freedom and Dignity.* I propose to expose these confusions we have concerning the negative features of Brave New World societies which have been at the root of much Dystopian literature. For the sake of the argument, I shall take the side of the defenders of Brave New World societies, though I think that in the long run their position turns out to be inadequate.

What is Wrong with Brave New Worlds?

What is wrong with Brave New World societies (BNWs)? We might answer: BNWs are among the most totalitarian of totalitarian societies, the most slavish of slave societies. Like other totalitarian societies, BNWs are governed by a small elite which settles authoritatively all the major social issues, and in the process exerts enormous control over the nonrulers. But BNW ruling elites have an edge over all previous totalitarian ruling elites. They have enormous control, not only over the behavior of their subjects, but also over their wants and needs. They not only get their subjects to behave as they want them to behave, they also get them to want what they, the ruling elites, want them to want. The control of the BNW ruling elites intrudes into the innermost psychological depths of their subjects. In traditional totalitarian societies, the rulers might get the requisite performance from their subjects, but not always their love or their loyalty. The BNW rulers not only get performance; they also get universal loyalty, and even some kind of love. The BNW subjects are slaves and do not know it, or they may even enjoy it. For example, they willingly choose the vocations which their rulers have programed them to have, and they willingly die at the time that their rulers have programed them to die.

But precisely what is wrong with totalitarian societies? The obvious answer is that they are necessarily unfree, if we assume freedom to be a good thing, perhaps the thing of highest value. To this, defenders of the BNW "ideal" (such as B. F. Skinner) respond in one of two ways. They sometimes take the path of least resistance and argue that freedom is not such a good thing after all, or indeed that it is a bad thing. Political freedom, they say, is incompatible with the maximization of human domination of nature, with the promotion of high production and affluence, with sound education, and with mental health and happiness. But this response does not work against those of us who are willing to subordinate domination of nature, sound education, and even some happiness, to freedom. However, Skinner and his allies sometimes take another strategy; they argue that BNW societies will be, paradoxically, more free than any other societies that will have existed before them. They tell us, in fact, that BNWs, as the most totalitarian of totalitarian societies, will be the freest of societies. And, surprisingly, the following very strong case can be made for the freedom of BNWs.

Totalitarianism and Freedom

Where do we, along with Dystopian writers, go wrong in our spontaneous and unhesitant belief that BNWs, as maximally totalitarian societies, are maximally unfree? According to such defenders of BNWs as Skinner, it all has to do with our lack of appreciation of the important differences among the various kinds of totalitarian societies and among the various kinds of freedom.

First, consider the various kinds of totalitarian societies. To exhibit the connection between unfreedom and totalitarianism we are most apt to point to societies like Stalinist Russia, Nazi Germany, and most recently military societies such as those of Brazil, Chile, and, formerly, Greece. Skinner and his allies have been quick to point out that these modern dictatorships are not really BNWs or anything like them; they are really old-fashioned dictatorships, with old-fashioned ruling groups (generals, party commissars, capitalists, religious fanatics, racists, etc.) and old-fashioned techniques of control (incarceration, torture, intimidation). But BNW dictators, we are reminded, are not capitalists, fascists, Stalinists, or militarists. They are not driven by greed, aggression, or pride. They do not seek to monopolize privileges, and they are not psychotic or megalomaniac.

BNWs are dictatorships by technocrats; they are dictatorships by scientists, engineers, and other experts. The source of technocratic power is knowledge, not wealth or ideological fervor. Technocrats want order, efficiency, and maximal control over nature and history; they think that misery and poverty are dysfunctional relative to these ends and therefore want happiness and affluence for all. Technocrats do not assert their power through the use of crude, painful, and inefficient techniques of old, such as incarceration and torture; they resort to the more scientific and benign techniques of behavioral engineering, such as conditioning and pharmacological, electrophysiological, and genetic manipulation.

Next, consider the variations in types of freedom. Some freedoms are nonpolitical (such as freedom from divine predestination, freedom from fate, freedom from natural laws, freedom from one's genes and one's environment), and others are political (such as freedom from coercion, freedom from manipulation, freedom to vote, freedom to worship if and as one chooses). Some freedoms are negative, and others positive; any freedom *from* something is a negative freedom, such as freedom from want, freedom from fear, and freedom from sin; and any freedom *to do* or *to be* something is a positive freedom, such as the freedom to own property, the freedom to be one's master, the freedom to do as one pleases. Some freedoms are important, others unimportant. Some are achievable, and others in principle unachievable. In evaluating any society in terms of the amount of freedom it allows we are interested mainly in political freedoms which are achievable and important. A political freedom does not appear to be important if it does not entail some positive freedom; that is, a political freedom *from* something does not appear important if it is not also, or does not entail, a freedom *to be* or *to do* something.

Skinner and other defenders of BNWs argue against Dystopian critics not that BNWs maximize every conceivable type of freedom, but rather, that they maximize all those political freedoms which are achievable and important. And, as far as pure or ideal BNWs go, I think these defenders clearly win the argument against the Dystopian critics. That this is so I will establish in detail.

There are at least three kinds of freedom which are normally taken quite seriously and which are thought to be virtually absent or minimized in any Brave New World. They are freedom from coercion, freedom from necessity, and freedom from external control. In the remainder of this chapter, I shall explain each of these kinds of freedom. I shall attempt to show that BNWs, were they to exist, could not be easily criticized for lacking these freedoms. This will expose some of the latent confusions of the standard Dystopian literature, which we all share at some time or other. For each of these freedoms, it seems to me a plausible case can be made that the freedom in question is maximized in pure or ideal Brave New World societies, or that though absent in BNWs it is also absent everywhere else, or that though absent in BNWs it is no longer important or desirable.

Freedom from Coercion

In order to maximize their control over the behavior of their subjects, dictatorial groups may resort to either coercive or noncoercive techniques. If the dictators resort to physical force, to commands and threats backed by legal sanctions, or to the infliction of pain and suffering in order to get their subjects to do what they want them to do, then they are making use of coercive techniques for controlling their subjects. Coercion, of course, is called for only when the subjects are not inclined to do what their leaders want them to do or to refrain from doing what their leaders do not want them to do. Insofar as they submit to coercive control, the subjects are prevented from doing everything that they want to do and from refraining from everything that they do not want to do.

In noncoercive control, on the other hand, the leaders are able to get their subjects to behave as they want them to behave without resorting to physical force, to punishment, or to the threat of punishment. They get their subjects to behave as required either by rewarding them for doing so or by internally engineering them (by chemical, physiological, or genetic means) to want to do so, to enjoy doing so, or to intrinsically value doing so. By the use of noncoercive techniques, the dictators in effect get the subjects to perform willingly what they are required to do and to refrain willingly from performing what they are prohibited from doing.

It so happens that when people have cried out for their freedom against tyrannical rule, they have in effect cried out for freedom from coercion. Their demand has been to be left alone, to pursue the politics, the religion, and the life-style of their choice; they have sought to restrict as much as is feasible the ability of governments to order them around, to subject them to threats, physical abuse, and incarceration, to interfere in their affairs, to regulate their activities, to appropriate their goods, and to lay obstacles in their paths. No doubt freedom from governmental coercion is a very important, and perhaps the most important, of political freedoms (if indeed not the only bona fide political freedom). Skinner emphasizes this strongly (through Frazier, his spokesperson in *Walden Two*):

> We have no vocabulary of freedom in dealing with what we want to do. . . . The question never arises. When men strike for freedom, they strike against jails and the police, or the threat of them—against oppression. They never strike against forces which make them want to act the way they do.[3]

Up to now, the most totalitarian societies (such as Czarist Russia, the Ottoman Empire, Nazi Germany, Stalinist Russia) have been the most coercive societies. This is because up to now coercion has been the primary instrument for exerting central authoritative control over citizen behavior. There has been a positive correlation between the amount of control ruling elites have exerted over their subjects and the amount of coercion they have exerted. Consequently, the most totalitarian societies have been the least free from political coercion, and the least totalitarian societies have been the most free from political coercion (as was postrevolutionary America).

Since BNWs are the most totalitarian of societies, one might expect that they would be the most coercive were they to exist. Such indeed is the projection of Orwell's *1984*. According to that work, the dictators of BNWs will maintain power mainly through fear, intimidation, physical constraint, psychological oppression, and torture—that is, mainly through coercion. Surprisingly, most writers do not accept this estimate. Generally, the most intransigent Dystopian critics of future BNWs (such as Huxley, Marcuse, and Ellul) as well as the apologists (such as Skinner), agree that dictatorial coercion will be eliminated in BNWs while dictatorial control will be maximized. Nonruling members will be subject to minimal coercion by others while subject to maximal control by others. It is generally assumed that the dictatorial elites of BNWs will resort almost exclusively to noncoercive techniques of control.

Huxley thinks that his "fairy tale" of the future society, in which dictators rule noncoercively, is more plausible than Orwell's "fairy tale," in which dictators rule coercively.

George Orwell's *1984* was a magnified projection into the future of a present that contained Stalinism and an immediate past that had witnessed the flowering of Nazism. In the context of 1948, when *1984* was published, *1984* seemed dreadfully convincing. But tyrants are moral and circumstances change. Recent developments in Russia and recent advances in science and technology have robbed Orwell's book of some of its gruesome verisimilitude. A nuclear war will, of course, make nonsense of everybody's predictions. But, assuming for the moment that the Great Powers can somehow refrain from destroying us, we can see that it looks as though the odds were more in favor of something like *Brave New World* than of something like *1984*.

The society described in *1984* is a society controlled almost exclusively by punishment and the fear of punishment. In the imaginary world of my own fable, punishment is infrequent and generally mild. The near perfect control exercised by the government is achieved by systematic reinforcement of desirable behavior, by many kinds of nearly nonviolent manipulation, both physical and psychological, and by genetic standardization.[4]

Herbert Marcuse concurs that the approaching BNW is not of the Orwellian kind:

A comfortable, smooth, reasonable, democratic unfreedom prevails in advanced industrial civilization, a token of technical progress. . . . By virtue of the way it has organized its technological base, contemporary industrial society tends to be totalitarian. For "totalitarian" is not only a terroristic political coordination of society, but also a non-terroristic economic-technical coordination which operates through the manipulation of needs by vested interests. It thus precludes the emergence of an effective opposition to the whole.[5]

Skinner likewise describes his fictitious society, Walden Two, as almost entirely free from coercion. He clearly thinks that this represents the wave of the future (again, in the words of Frazier, his fictitious spokesperson):

The question is: can men live in freedom and peace? And the answer is: yes, if we can build a social structure which will satisfy the needs of everyone and in which everyone will want to observe the supporting code. But so far this has been achieved only in Walden Two. Your ruthless accusations to the contrary, Mr. Castle [Frazier's antagonist], this is the freest place on earth. And it is free precisely because we make no use of force or the threat of force. By skillful planning, by a wise choice of techniques we *increase* the feeling of freedom.[6]

Yet, central planning and behavior control are maximized in Walden Two:

> We can achieve a sort of control under which the controlled, though they are following a code more scrupulously than was ever the case under the old system, nevertheless *feel free*. They are doing what they want to do, not what they are forced to do. . . . By a careful cultural design, we control not the behavior, but the inclination to behave—the motives, the desires, the wishes. . . . No, Mr. Castle, when a science of behavior has once been achieved, there's no alternative to a planned society. We can't leave mankind to an accidental or biased control.[7]

In Skinner's version of the BNW, the primary instrument of political control is positive reinforcement. The members of Walden Two acquire from early childhood the requisite attitudes and behavioral repertoires by being rewarded rather than punished. In Huxley's version, the primary instruments of control are genetic engineering and Pavlovian conditioning. For example, the leaders for the most part do not have to resort to prohibitions backed by sanctions (such as threats of jail or death) in order to prevent the citizenry from falling in love, from getting married, or from bearing children. Rather, the leaders have manipulated the genes of the citizenry so that people will be thoroughly disgusted by the very ideas of love, marriage, and parenthood, and the leaders have supplemented this with a variety of painless brainwashing techniques.

According to this more standard account (that of Huxley, Marcuse, and Skinner), the nonruling members of BNWs, while under the maximal control of the rulers, will paradoxically be almost perfectly free from coercion. In doing what they are controlled to do, they will be doing exactly what they want to do. The leaders of BNWs normally will not make their subjects act against their wills, since the rulers control their subjects' wills as well as their acts. According to the standard account, BNWs cannot justifiably be criticized for lacking freedom from coercion.

The startling conclusion that BNWs maximize freedom from coercion requires some defense. Why is it that the ruling elites of BNWs, unlike the ruling elites of past dictatorial societies, will tend to resort almost exclusively to noncoercive rather than coercive means of control? The answer usually given (such as by Skinner) is quite simply the following. The technocratic rulers of BNWs are interested in using only the most efficient techniques of control. Punishment is simply not an efficient technique of control. Punished persons will secretly desire to do, and when unsupervised will attempt to do, what they were punished for doing and will furthermore develop neuroses and anxieties which will make them less predictable and reliable. Skinner asserts, "We are gradually discovering—at an untold cost in human suffering—that in the long run punishment doesn't reduce the probability that an act will occur."[8] Huxley concurs:

> It has become clear that control through the punishment of undesirable behavior is less effective, in the long run, than control through the reinforcement of desirable behavior by rewards, and that government through terror works on the whole less well than government through the non-violent manipulation of the environment and of the thoughts and feelings of individual men, women and children. Punishment temporarily puts a stop to undesirable behavior, but does not permanently reduce the victim's tendency to indulge in it. Moreover, the psychophysical by-products of punishment may be just as undesirable as the behavior for which an individual has been punished.[9]

Consequently, we can expect that technocratic rulers, being primarily interested in efficiency, will resort primarily to nonpunitive techniques of control (such as reward or genetic engineering) in order to get their subjects to do what they want them to do. That is, we can expect technocratic ruling elites of BNWs to use noncoercive rather than coercive techniques in order to exercise more efficient control over their subjects. More traditional kinds of ruling elites, such as the feudal nobility, have been less interested in efficiency. Also, until quite recently many forms of noncoercive control (such as the use of drugs) were just not technically feasible.

That coercive control is less effective than certain forms of non-coercive control is dramatically demonstrated by the following example. Consider the case of Jones, a trained riveter who has a fear of heights. How can those in charge get him to work on the construction of skyscrapers? They can, of course, resort to coercion. They can threaten him with incarceration, unemployment, torture, or even death if he refuses to work on the construction of skyscrapers, but this

solution is not satisfactory. As long as Jones's fear of heights is uncon-
quered, he will be barely able to tolerate his work. He will always be
tempted to come in late for work, to leave early, to take long lunch
breaks, to spend as much time as possible near the ground, and to take
sick leaves; no matter how frightful the possible punishment, Jones will
always savor the prospect of walking off the job permanently. He will
also suffer from fears and anxieties which detract from the attention and
skill he should bring to his job, which disrupt his leisure and social life,
and which make him prone to be intractable, unpredictable, or uncon-
trollable in other life situations.

Suppose, however, that through the use of pharmacological or
electrophysiological techniques the bosses are able not only to eliminate his fear of heights, but also to get him actually to enjoy being in
high places. Their ability to control Jones's work behavior is enhanced
considerably, because Jones now wants to do what they want him to
do. Since Jones now enjoys working in high places, he goes about his
work with enthusiasm, perhaps being the first in the morning to reach
the top of the building under construction and the last to come down in
the evening. He may work through lunch breaks and even show up at
the site when slightly sick. There is no temptation on his part to pursue
another occupational line, even should his pay not be fully satisfactory.
He now has no job-related anxieties or fears which distract him from
his work, make him uncooperative, or disrupt his personal and social
life.

Obviously, if the costs are not prohibitive it is more effective to
control Jones's work activity by the use of noncoercive techniques
(getting Jones to want and value highly the behavior he is controlled to
exhibit) than by coercive techniques (such as punishment or the threat
thereof). Consequently, if we assume that technocratic elites are committed to maximizing the effectivenss of their control over their subjects (which seems reasonable), and we assume that in BNWs of the
future the technologies of noncoercive control will be highly developed
and moderately priced (which again seems reasonable), then we can
conclude that technocratic ruling elites of BNWs will tend to maximize
the noncoercive control they exercise over their subjects and minimize the coercive control that they so exercise. This means that in
all probability the subjects of the most advanced BNWs would be
nearly completely free from coercion and hence completely free to do
what they want. This would be no mean achievement.

The Machine-like Character of BNW Members

Suppose we (as do many Dystopians) conceded that in BNWs there would be full freedom from coercion and full freedom to do as one pleases. We (along with Dystopian critics of BNWs) would still not be satisfied. We would most probably find this freedom possessed by BNW members to be very superficial; we would say that the BNW members have completely lost touch with the truly basic and ennobling kinds of freedom. Our reasoning might go something like this. People in the BNWs are no doubt free to do what they want most or value most highly, but they are not free in wanting what they want, or in valuing what they value. They are not free to reject or transform their basic wants and basic values, for their basic wants and basic values have been programed into them by their rulers. The nonruling members may have control over what they do, but they do not have control over what they want or what they value. Only their programers, the technocrats, are in a position to control what they, the programed nonrulers, will want and value. The nonruling members are like automatons, and like automatons, they have no autonomy. In the "deep" sense of the term, they have no real freedom.

So goes the objection. Though BNW members are "superficially" free (free from coercion), they are "deeply" unfree in the same sense in which automatons or machines are unfree. But in what sense are machines or automatons unfree?

Traditionally, machines or automatons have been thought to be unfree in at least two ways. First, machines are unfree from necessity. Machines are governed by deterministic laws. Everything that a machine does is the inevitable and necessary consequence of its previous internal states (such as the connections between its wires) and its previous inputs (such as the pressing of various buttons). Indeed, everything that a machine does is the inevitable and necessary consequence of its original internal states (including its original program) in conjunction with the temporal sequence of inputs which have occurred since then. Given its original constitution and subsequent inputs, it is impossible for the machine to do anything else. Insofar as a machine is necessarily what it is, given its previous inputs and internal states, then a machine can be said to be unfree from necessity. As artificial systems, machines, whatever be their native "intelligence," are essentially at the service of other intelligent beings (presumably humans); they are designed, created, overseen, controlled, and manipulated by these intelligent beings. They perform tasks only because someone has decided that they should do so and only because their doing so fits in with someone else's plans and contributes to the attainment of his or her objectives. It is an essential mark of machines that their functioning is virtually under the complete control of intelligent (presumably human) beings. In this sense, machines are unfree from external control by other intelligent beings.

No doubt the nonruling members of ideal BNWs are completely unfree from necessity and from external control. For what they are and how they behave is completely determined by their genes and environment; hence, they are unfree from necessity. Furthermore, they are under the complete control of their rulers and, hence, are completely unfree from external control by others. Having to concede this, the defenders of BNWs can only respond that these freedoms are either unachievable anywhere else or no longer politically important. I think this response can be maintained quite plausibly, as I shall show in the following sections.

Freedom from Necessity

It could be argued that no humans are or can be free from necessity and, hence, that BNWs cannot justifiably be blamed for lacking it.

First, it is scientifically quite respectable to assume that the psychic states of human beings, as well as their behavior, are completely determined by the interaction of their genes and the environment. Humans are organisms, and organisms are macrophysical objects (are larger than molecules or are very large molecules). The states of inanimate macrophysical objects seem to be completely determined by previous states of these objects and of the surrounding universe; at least this is what science tells us. There is strong evidence that nonhuman organisms are also governed by deterministic laws, that is, by laws specifying that states of a certain sort are the inevitable and necessary outcomes of previous states of other sorts. There is no strong evidence for concluding that humans, alone among all organismic macrophysical entities, are not wholly governed by deterministic laws.

Be that as it may, at least this much can be said: if we allow that

BNWs are possible (as Dystopians do), then we must conclude that human beings generally are unfree from necessity. The possibility of BNWs presupposes that human mental states and behavior are completely determined by human genes and previous states of the environment, for the rulers of BNWS exercise virtually complete control over the beliefs, wants, and acts of the nonruling members. This they can achieve only indirectly; that is, BNW rulers can exercise complete control over the beliefs, wants, and acts of the nonruling members by exercising complete control over the genes and environments of the nonruling members. But this complete control over gene-environment interactions will not translate into complete control over beliefs, wants, and acts unless it is already the case, even before the rulers have intervened, that the gene-environment interactions of human beings completely determine their beliefs, wants, and acts. The deterministic relation between gene-environment interactions and subsequent mental states and acts is not brought about as a consequence of the exercise of power by the BNW rulers; rather, it is presupposed by that exercise of power. The BNW rulers do not cause genes and environments to determine the contents of minds and behavior. They are able rather to manipulate genes and environments successfully to achieve complete control over the contents of minds and behavior, but only because humans are already the sorts of beings whose mental and behavioral states necessarily and inevitably follow from the interaction of their genes and environments.

So either "pure" BNWs (BNWs where the ruling elites have virtually complete control over the thoughts and behavior of their subjects) are possible or they are not. But if they are possible (as we and the Dystopian critics seem to assume) this is in part because humans are not free from necessity. BNW leaders, no matter what their power, can never bring it about that humans are unfree from necessity; their completely successful exercise of power presupposes that we are unfree from necessity. If we are unfree from necessity, then this burden (if burden it be) is imposed on us by nature, not by other humans.

Consequently, it appears that if freedom from necessity is not achievable in a BNW, then it is not achievable in any other society either. Freedom from necessity is not a freedom which we can impose or take away by human contrivance. In this sense, it is not a political freedom and is not relevant to the discussion of alternative political societies.

Freedom from External Control

Brave New World societies offer virtually no freedom from external
control; in an ideal BNW the rulers have virtually complete control
over the nonruling population. There is certainly less freedom from
external control in BNWs than in any of the societies, even the most
dictatorial, which have existed in the past. Freedom from external
control is absent in BNWs, but it is achievable within limits in societies
other than BNWs.

Thus it appears Dystopians can justifiably criticize BNWs for lacking any freedom from external control. But the issue has not been won
yet. The defenders of BNWs have a response which is not easy to
overcome. They say that freedom from external control is no longer a
desirable or important political freedom (as in Skinner's *Beyond Freedom and Dignity*). What is the basis for this?

The defenders would no doubt admit that freedom from external
control was indispensable and important in traditional, technologically
backward societies as a means for enhancing freedom from coercion. In
these societies rulers exercised control through the use of force,
punishment, and the threat of punishment. In them, there has been a
direct correlation between the amount of external control exercised by
rulers over the subject population and the amount of coercion they
have imposed. Thus, the less freedom from external control the traditional subjects have had, the less freedom from coercion they have had.
Freedom from coercion in traditional societies has presupposed freedom from external control. Since freedom from coercion is and has
always been an important and desirable freedom, then (at least in
traditional, technologically backward societies) freedom from external
control (as an indispensable means for the attainment of freedom from
coercion) has also been an important and desirable freedom.

But this is no longer the case in technologically advanced societies
of the present or future, according to the defenders of BNWs. Here
rulers can most effectively control their subjects by using noncoercive
means, that is, by subtly getting their subjects to want to do and to
enjoy doing what the rulers require them to do; the use of threats and
punishment can be virtually eliminated as an instrument of control.
With the advance of modern technology, it is possible to institute
BNWs in which the complete absence of any freedom from external

control is accompanied by the maximization of freedom from coercion. In advanced technological societies, freedom from external control is not an indispensable means for achieving freedom from coercion; that is, freedom from external control is no longer important and desirable as a means for eliminating coercion.

We must remember also that in an ideal BNW the nonruling members, though fully controlled, are virtually completely content. This is not because the BNW technocratic rulers are lovers of humanity, but rather because it is easier to control contented people than discontented people. That the nonruling members are generally content is due to the way they are programed. General contentment is possible only when the wants and needs of the population have been harmonized. If everyone wants the same job, the same status, or the same scarce good; if everyone is competitive, aggressive, or spiteful; if all this is the case, then of course not everyone will be content. The BNW rulers thus program into their subjects only wants which are in harmony with one another and refrain from programing in "antisocial" wants, such as the desire to compete or to fight. The fact that there is little or no misery in BNWs and that there is some form of general happiness is therefore due to the fact that the wants and needs of BNW members are systematically and almost completely controlled by the rulers. Hence, the happiness and contentment of the nonruling members is a consequence of their lack of any freedom from external control.

It would then appear, contrary to what Dystopians would say, that in a world of advanced technology the presence of freedom from external control is no longer an indispensable condition for the preservation of obviously important freedoms (such as freedom from coercion), and that the elimination of freedom from external control has certain good results (such as the harmonization of needs and general contentment).

But if all this is true, if members of BNWs, though completely controlled by others, are generally uncoerced and content, then why is it bad for them to lack the freedom from external control? I said before that a freedom from something is not worth anything if it is not also, or if it does not entail, a freedom to be or do something. (Freedom from coercion, for example, entails the freedom to do as one pleases.) So the question arises: what is it that the nonruling members of ideal BNWs would be free to do if they were given freedom from external control which they are not free to do without it? The obvious answer might be: what the nonruling members are not free to do is to exercise internal control over their own lives. Since they are controlled by others, they cannot control themselves. Is this necessarily true?

To say that I have "internal" control over my behavior is apparently to say that my behavior springs from my own choices and wants, that these choices and wants are governed by principles which I have internalized, and that I am willing and able periodically to criticize and even change my principles of action. It seems to me possible to build a BNW in which the populace generally does what it has chosen to do, generally chooses this on the basis of principles and reasons, and periodically critically assesses these principles and perhaps changes them. For if a BNW is possible, there is no freedom from necessity for anyone, and if there is no freedom from necessity for anyone, then all our wants and choices, our deliberations and reasoning, and our principles are determined ultimately by the interaction of our genes and environments. Either this means that we really do not exercise internal control over our behavior when we choose, deliberate, and assess our principles or that our "internal control" or our "self-control" is itself determined by our genes and environments. If the former answer is correct, then no people, whether in or out of BNWs, can exercise internal control over their behavior and their lives; if the latter is correct, then members of BNWs can have just as much self-control over their behavior as members of other allegedly free societies.

If the way we internally control our behavior, through choices, deliberations, and applied principles, is determined by our genes and our environment, then paradoxically the way in which we internally control our behavior can be controlled externally by others. Take, for example, my choice to become a carpenter, my reasoning about becoming a carpenter, and my vocational principles, such as the principle that I ought to pick the kind of job most conducive to my physical health. If my choice to become a carpenter, my reasoning about this choice, and my principle to pick the physically healthiest job are determined by the presence of a particular arrangement of genes and environments, then this choice, these reasonings, and the internalization of that principle might have been induced in me by any behavioral engineer who properly manipulated my genes and environments. This could be induced in anyone else to whom some behavioral engineer gave the proper arrangement of genes and environments.

Furthermore, by properly arranging my genes and environments, the behavioral engineer could get me to question my vocational principle or even to reject it if it fails to satisfy some other principle, and so on. As a consequence of genetic-environmental engineering, I might in the appropriate circumstances ask myself whether I should pick an occupation that was most physically healthy if it prevented me thereby from properly supporting my family. So it appears that a BNW-type ruler might engineer me to exercise internal control over my behavior: I would choose what I do (my behavior would not simply appear compulsively); I would carefully weigh my decision (and thus not act rashly or irrationally); and I would examine my principles of action (so as not to behave dogmatically), but my behavior ultimately would be no less determined or controlled by others than that of a compulsive, rash, and dogmatic person who presumably exhibits no internal control over his or her behavior.

In conclusion, any sort of behavior which is completely determined by the agent's genes and environments is completely controllable by some person other than the agent. But BNWs are not possible unless it is generally the case that human behavior is completely determined in this way. Thus, the behavior of the "self-controlled" person is just as controllable and open to manipulation as is the behavior of a person lacking self-control. Depending on how he or she brings together the genes and environments of nonruling members, the BNW ruler can create either self-controlled or nonself-controlled persons (e.g., kleptomaniacs). And supposing that the BNW ruler has decided to create self-controlled persons, he or she can further choose which kind of self-controlled person to bring into existence by selecting from the various combinations of genes and environments which induce particular forms of self-controlled behavior. So the BNW ruler, by appropriately manipulating genes and environments, can create the kind of self-controlled person who will perform exactly the kinds of behavior wanted.

Consequently, there appear to be no good reasons in the abstract why ruling elites of BNWs, in order to maximize their power, should choose for their subjects the sorts of gene-environment complexes which induce compulsive actions, compulsive choices, or the uncritical acceptance of principles, rather than choosing the sorts of gene-environment complexes which induce choice-governed actions, reason-governed choices, and the critical acceptance of principles. The ruling elites can exercise just as much control over their subjects' choice-governed actions, reason-governed choices, and critical acceptance of principles as they can over their subjects' compulsive actions, compulsive choices, and uncritical acceptance of principles.

It is not difficult to conceive of ways in which nonruling members of BNWs, like certain kinds of automatons, might be programed to exercise internal control over their acts. The rulers of BNWs control the behavior of their subjects by controlling their choices, but they need not, and indeed would not, control these choices by randomly imposing them on their subjects. Such a procedure would be unbelievably unwieldly. Rather, through genetic engineering and the manipulation of the internal and external environments, they would program into their subjects the general rules governing the making of choices in various circumstances. Or they might better still program only the generally higher-level rules which guide the selection of first-level rules, which in turn guide the selection of choices. In the latter case, they might program in directly only the ultimate objectives the subjects are to pursue or the rules to prize most highly, leaving it up to the subjects to determine through experience (through the "contingencies of reinforcement) which subordinate rules or values will most effectively contribute to the implementation of the primary rules or values. Thus, nonruling members of a Brave New World need not be like adding machines whose every move is triggered by an outside command, nor like computers whose every move is determined by a set of pregiven general instructions. Nonruling members perhaps would be more like game-playing machines or pattern-recognition machines whose program for strategies and rules keep changing in the light of preprogramed ultimate objectives and continued negative and positive reinforcement. It is true that programers of game-playing machines do not determine explicitly every rule that these machines will follow, but it is misleading to say that they thereby have less control over the machines than do computer programers over computers. For they control the contingencies of reinforcement, and as long as they get the machines to achieve the objectives they want, then they have full control. Indeed, for complex tasks it is much more effective for programers (or dictators) to deal with automatons (or subjects) which are plastic, adaptive, and self-regulative than with those which are not. That is, it is much more effective for the programers (or rulers) to deal with automatons (or subjects) which, while fulfilling their objectives, require of them a minimum of attention and intervention.

A self-controlled person may be controllable in much the same way that a game-playing machine—or any other sort of plastic, adaptive, and self-regulative machine—is controllable. In the performance of complex tasks, self-controlled persons are superior to persons having no self-control for the same sorts of reasons that game-playing machines are superior to mere calculating machines. Thus there is little doubt that any well-run BNW would include a large number of self-controlled nonruling subjects.

The compatibility between being externally controlled and exercising internal control is further illustrated by the fact that, at least in Huxley's BNW, the procedures of external control are mainly applied to factors on which, or contexts in which, the subject could not conceivably have had any internal control. External control is effected mainly through genetic engineering and the classical conditioning of young children, but neither of these procedures rob their subjects of any potential internal control. You cannot determine your genetic make-up at birth nor your environment in the early years following birth; you cannot choose your original character traits. The only difference between a BNW and a classical nontotalitarian society is that in the former case the genetic makeup and early environment of an individual are determined by human planning, and in the latter case they are a consequence of natural accidents and the vagaries of human interaction.

It may be objected that the practice of the so-called internally controlled members of BNWs of critically examining their basic principles is a meaningless ritual. These members are not free to reject or to rebel against the basic principles which have been inculcated in them, whereas at least some members of traditional nontotalitarian societies would be free to reject or to rebel against the basic values which have been inculcated in them. But this is a confusion. In one sense, members of BNWs are free to change their minds and to rebel; that is, they can if they want to, but they do not want to. (In this sense, they are free from coercion.) In the deeper sense in which they are unfree to change their minds and rebel, the rebels of nontotalitarian societies are similarly unfree not to change their minds and not to rebel; no one is free from necessity, neither the conformist who has been determined by genes and environments to be a conformist, nor the rebel who has been similarly determined to be a rebel.

It seems to me that the defenders of BNWs might thus conclude as follows. There is no correlation between freedom from external control on the one hand and the freedom to exercise internal control on the other. By being deprived of freedom from external control, the nonruling members of BNWs would not thereby be deprived of internal control or self-control. And there does not seem to be anything else which the members of ideal BNWs would be rendered unfree to do because of their lack of freedom from external control. From the point of view of the nonruling members of BNWs, the acquisition of freedom from external control would not involve the acquisition of any positive freedom, that is, any freedom to do or be something which they did not have before. Freedom from external control, for BNW members, would appear as a purely negative freedom; for them, it would be an unimportant, a useless, and even a damaging freedom.

The defenders of BNWs generally argue that BNWs cannot justifiably be criticized for lacking any important and achievable political freedom. Ideal BNWs would maximize freedom from coercion. They would totally lack freedom from necessity and freedom from external control. But if BNWs are possible, then freedom from necessity is unachievable anywhere, and the freedom from external control is no longer important or useful in advanced technological societies.

Ideal and Nonideal Brave New Worlds

In any abstract argument, the defenders of BNWs (such as Skinner) seem to beat out the Dystopian critics. Does this mean that our negative feelings about the dictatorial consequences of modern technology and concerning the prospect for the existence of Brave New Worlds are wholly confused and illusory? Could we have been so hopelessly misled? Our intuitions and feelings about Brave New Worlds are probably confused, but they are far from illusory. There is something offensive about defending the expected technological dictatorships of the future, but it is not easy to show precisely why it is offensive. Thus, the success of Skinner and his like.

Our negative feelings about future technological dictatorships, though in all probability basically right, are somewhat misdirected. We focus on ideal BNWs, that is, BNWs in which all decisions are made by "pure" technicians, in which only noncoercive techniques of behavior control are used, in which all scarcity has been eliminated, in which happiness prevails, and in which dull moronic work is carried out exclusively by machines. Ideal or pure BNWs are utopias of sorts, and it is difficult to show what is bad about them. But they are also highly improbable; indeed, we might say with a good deal of confidence that nothing like an ideal or pure BNW will ever exist. What we have a right to fear are not these imaginary utopian BNWs, but those more probable "half-baked" or "mixed" or "intermediate" BNWs in which technocrats either share power with or are willing functionaries of capitalists, generals, or party bureaucrats, in which crude techniques of coercive control still must be resorted to (as in Orwell's *1984*), in which scarcity prevails, and in which humans must perform alienating and mindless jobs. There is considerable probability that new technological techniques (such as new armaments, new information-gathering devices, and new discoveries in the control of human fear) will favor the rise of dictatorships of this mixed sort. There is already a bit of the nonideal Brave New World in modern political and commercial advertising, in the capers of Watergate-style presidents and their advisors, in the domestic and foreign adventures of the CIA and FBI, in the organization of centralized data banks, in the mass propaganda techniques of the Soviet Union, and in the new technologies for torturing or intimidating political prisoners (as is done in the Soviet Union and Brazil).

BNWs of this mixed sort of course should be feared; we can well conceive the horrors which they may perpetuate. The defenders of BNWs win the argument because both they and their opponents assume the probability of a completely utopian dictatorial system. A utopian dictatorship might be quite fine, and perhaps better than most nondictatorial but nonutopian societies. We can be fairly sure, though, that no such thing will ever take place. It is highly improbable that behavioral technology will sufficiently develop in the foreseeable future to allow complete noncoercive control by rulers over the behavior and minds of their subject populations. Furthermore, it is quite improbable that a group of dictatorial rulers can be generated which will overwhelmingly prefer the use of noncoercive rather than coercive methods of control. Finally, we come to the fundamental assumption underlying the prediction of the emergence of an ideal BNW—the assumption that technocrats are wresting power over politics and economics from capitalists, Communist party bureaucrats, or army generals. In chapter 4, I showed this assumption to be quite plausible, but I will come back to it in chapter 11. Here I will present the devastating Socialist refutation of the claim that in America technocrats are in the process of wresting power away from the capitalists. Once the assumption of technocratic control is rejected, then the prediction that modern societies are in the process of being transformed into pure or ideal BNWs must also be rejected. Dictatorships may well be on the rise universally (as Robert Heilbroner bleaky forecasts in his *Inquiry into the Human Prospect*), but if so they are of the capitalist or socialist or military kind, not of the technocratic kind. Technologically sophisticated, nontechnocratic dictatorships (in which the services of technocrats are used by the ruling groups) may share something of the nature of BNWs, but at best they are mixed or half-baked BNWs. We should be appalled by all dictatorships, present or future, not because we would find even a Utopian dictatorship (such as an ideal or pure BNW) to be bad, but because we have good reason to believe that no utopian dictatorship or ideal BNW will ever exist, and we do know that nonutopian dictatorships are bad. In expressing our fears about the political impact of modern technology, we have let ourselves be misdirected both by the Dystopian critics and the defenders of future technocratic societies into focusing these fears on dictatorial societies which will never exist, and which we ought not to fear if they were to exist.

Conclusion

I have critically examined the Classical Dystopian position on modern technology. Classical Dystopians say that modern technology is leading to the emergence of a new sort of dictatorship, a technocratic dictatorship which ultimately will take the form of a pure Brave New World. Their criticims I have shown to be refutable because they are misdirected. Pure BNWs cannot be shown to be unfree for those freedoms (like the freedom from coercion) which are achievable and important.

By allowing that human contentment will tend to prevail, that coercion will be eliminated, and that moronic jobs will be automated, they conceded all the important points to the defenders of the future technological dictatorships. Had they not done this, their case would have been much stronger.

Notes

[1]See chapter 1, notes 3 and 4.
[2]Aldous Huxley, *Brave New World Revisited* (New York: Bantam, 1960), pp. 1–2.
[3]B. F. Skinner, *Walden Two* (New York: Macmillan, 1948), p. 263.
[4]Huxley, *Brave New World Revisted*, pp. 2–3.
[5]Herbert Marcuse, *One Dimensional Man* (Boston: Beacon, 1964), pp. 1–3.
[6]B. F. Skinner, *Walden Two* (Boston: Beacon, 1964), p. 263.
[7]Ibid., p. 262.
[8]Ibid., p. 260.
[9]Huxley, *Brave New World Revisited*, p. 3.

7

Sexual Alienation

The Countercultural Dystopian view is very much "in the air." It is an outgrowth of the youth movements of the 1960s. It is associated with the beat generation, with hippies and Yippies; it has been supported by spokesmen of the consciousness and sexual revolutions. This is not to say that all hippies, Yippies, and consciousness revolutionaries are technological Dystopians. But many are, at least in some vague and confused way, and it seems appropriate that they should be.

The Meaning of Alienation

Countercultural Dystopians have tended to blame technology for much of the allegedly bad things that have been done to our psyches, our consciousness, our "heads." They criticize technology for its allegedly deleterious psychological effects. It is sometimes put this way: while increasing our material wealth and our domination of nature, technology has created in us more and more alienation; we are increasingly alienated from our bodies, from our work, from others, and from nature. To understand the Countercultural critique of modern technology, we have to understand why it is thought that technology has made us more and more alienated.

We should first get a clearer sense of the meaning, or meanings, of the word "alienation." Much has been said about alienation recently, most of it confusing and unhelpful. One gets the impression from the mystifying claims made by scholars and theoreticians that questions concerning the nature of alienation are very difficult and require a deep answer. This seems wrong to me. As I see it, "alienation" is simply a code word for a number of easily defined forms of individual frustration and social dysfunction. Obscurity and mystery enter when investigators attempt to specify the distinguishing characteristics common to all instances of alienation. The truth is, the word "alienation" has a number of different but overlapping meanings; there is no common meaning underyling all its uses. Once this is appreciated, the mystery surrounding its use disappears.

As I see it, there are three types of alienation referred to, or three broad meanings of alienation operating, in Countercultural critiques of technology. They are the alienation from self, the alienation from others, and the alienation from nature. Let me say something briefly about each of these.

ALIENATION FROM SELF

The alienation from one's self is exemplified either in the alienation from one's activity or the alienation from the product of one's activity. Consider a particular activity, and suppose that humans generally do not enjoy doing it, and avoid doing it whenever possible, though they may be compelled on a regular basis; that they have no control over the way they are to do it, and are serving someone else's interest rather than their own; that they are bored and perform the activity mechanically; that it is unchallenging and without social significance; and that they do not at present have the opportunity or capacity to do this activity in a fulfilling manner. If most of the above conditions are met, then humans would be "alienated" from this activity. If true human satisfaction is impossible or incomplete without the performance of this particular activity, then humans can be emancipated from their alienation only by learning, and being allowed, to perform it in a truly fulfilling manner. If this activity is always incompatible with complete satisfaction, then humans will be emancipated only when the conditions which make this activity necessary are eliminated.

Taking their cue from Sigmund Freud and Karl Marx, the Countercultural Dystopians have focused on work and sex as the two major forms of alienated activity. Humans are forced to perform exhausting, insignificant, and boring labor; they are socialized to abstain from exactly those forms of sensuous experience which are truly fulfilling, leaving as alternatives the performance either of actions devoid of sensuous content or of sexual actions which are mechanical and unsatisfying. The sexual alienation will be overcome presumably when humans "recover their bodies and their senses," that is, when they learn to infuse everything that they do with real sensuous consciousness. However, on the question of the emancipation from the alienation of labor, the Countercultural humanists side with Freud against Marx. According to them, there will be alienation as long as humans continue to labor, presumably because of the inherent tension between work and sexual liberation. In the unalienated state, it will be all play and no work. What systematically differentiates the Counterculture further from Marx and Freud is its tendency to impute the alienation of labor and sex to the imperatives of institutionalized technology, rather than to class exploitation or to civilization as such.

The alienation from self also finds expression in the alienation from the product of one's activity. Humans are alienated from their own product if it is used by others to exploit or manipulate them, or if it acquires a life of its own and in turn comes to dominate its producers. Such, according to Karl Marx, is the condition of the worker who is exploited through the commodity which he produces. According to the nineteenth-century atheist philosopher Ludwig Feuerbach, it is also the condition of the religious persons dominated by their own artifacts (namely, God and religion) and who have imputed to those artifacts their own potentialities. In this spirit, Countercultural Dystopians have maintained that we are alienated from our own technology as an object of our activity. We have lost control over institutionalized technology; the development of organization and machinery, according to them, is now autonomous and unimpedable. Technology has a life of its own, and we serve it rather than direct it.

ALIENATION FROM OTHERS

If humans are continually in conflict with one another; if they manipulate one another, or exhibit little care for the needs and feelings of others; if individuals are isolated from others, lonely, and lost; if societies are massified or homogenized—if any or all of these conditions hold, then humans are alienated from one another. According to the Counterculture, contemporary technology and its institutionalized values are the causes of a large number of types of social alienation, such as personal detachment, disrespect for the privacy of others, the experimental manipulation of others, conformism, consumerism (orientation toward things rather than people), the subordination of the individual to the organization, the decreasing social importance of the individual, the increasing role of machines in mediating between people and things, anonymity and isolation, the deemphasis of permanent relationships between persons, the demise of traditional communities (such as the family), mass society and cultural homogenation, and the rise of the warfare state.

ALIENATION FROM NATURE

This concept is somewhat metaphorical and it is constructed on the model of the alienation from others. To the extent that it makes sense to say that people are oppressing, exploiting, or dominating nature, or that they have lost all feel for, or intimacy with nature, or that they disrespectfully disrupt natural processes, or that they are no longer at home in nature, or that they are no longer properly integrated with nature or within natural systems, then it makes sense to say that people are alienated from nature.

Countercultural thinkers have claimed that there are at least two kinds of alienation from nature caused or reinforced by technology, its growth, and its values. First, modern technological growth has led to the growth of cities, increasingly surrounding people with artifacts and cutting them off from untouched, or barely modified, natural environments. The Countercultural response to this is a new kind of primitivism advocating a return to rural living, self-sufficiency, and a minimal dependence on artifacts. Second, the pursuit of modern technological values (technological rationality) has created increasing ecological disruption in the form of pollution, population growth, and the depletion of nonrenewable resources. The only answer to this, according to Countercultural Dystopians, is to eliminate all forms of growth—population growth, economic growth, and even technological growth.

In the next four chapters, I shall examine some of these alleged

kinds of alienation caused by the imperatives of modern technology. I
shall especially concentrate on the alienations from self and from nature, though talking about these two kinds of alienation will involve
talking about alienation from others.

The Playboy Syndrome

Among the many problems which it has attacked, the Countercultural
youth movement has directed most of its energy at sexual alienation,
which it assumes to be widespread and deep. Its call has been primarily for sexual liberation. Its adherents have continually exhorted us to
overcome our repressions, "uptightness," desensitization, and alienation from our bodies. In opposition to Marxist radicals, Countercultural
radicals stress the primacy of sexual alienation over social alienation.
While Marxists claim that alienation from oneself (including sexual
alienation) is rooted in social alienation (such as exploitation, oppression, and objectification of others), Countercultural Dystopians claim
that social alienation is rooted in alienation from oneself, and especially, in sexual alienation. According to the former, we must be emancipated socioeconomically before we can be emancipated sexually; according to the latter, we must be emancipated sexually before we can
be emancipated socioeconomically.

On this theme, the Countercultural youth movement has been
greatly influenced by the work of Wilhelm Reich, Paul Goodman,
Norman O. Brown, and Herbert Marcuse, all of whom have given
sexuality a central place in their analysis of the illnesses of modern
societies. The movement, however, claims to have added new dimen-
sions to this analysis, which theorists like Theodore Roszak, Charles
Reich, and Philip Slater have attempted to capture (though not always
successfully).

It is not clear what Countercultural Dystopians take sexual liberation to be. To find out, we must first determine what they mean by
"sexual alienation." This is no easy matter, for their conception of
sexual alienation is somewhat complicated and unusual.

Clearly this much is true. Anyone who is not capable of enjoying
sex in its socially harmless forms, or who is not willing or allowed to do
so, is alienated from sex. This kind of sexual alienation exists when

there are social taboos against premarital sex, or against nonstandard sexual practices (such as oral sex); it exists where people feel deeply guilty about sex, or treat it merely as a means for procreation. In the past one hundred years, but especially since the appearance of Sigmund Freud's work, a number of groups have propagandized for the elimination of sexual taboos and sexual guilt, and for the liberation of sex from its purely procreative function. Countercultural Dystopians clearly are not the first to struggle against sexual alienation, nor are they the only ones doing so today. We are presently undergoing a major sexual revolution of which the Countercultural youth movement is only a part.

But it would be wrong to see the Countercultural movement simply as a repetition of past movements for sexual liberation, or to submerge it undifferentially in the present sexual revolution. It would be especially wrong to interpret the Countercultural movement merely as a response to the recalcitrant remnants of puritanical taboos and guilt obsessions in our society. This interpretation would force us to group together in the same movement people whose sexual attitudes are radically different. For example, imagine bracketing jet-setters and playboys (or playgirls) with hippies, or mate-swapping clubs with communes. To ensure accuracy, it is better to speak of two ongoing sexual revolutions, the first embodied in life-styles exemplified by such magazines as *Playboy* and *Playgirl,* and the second embodied in Countercultural life-styles; the first arising in opposition to the old restrictive moralities, and the second in opposition to the new sexual permissiveness of playboy and playgirl sex as well as to the old restrictive moralities. For Countercultural Dystopians, both the sexual restraints of the middle American and the sexual promiscuities of the playboy and playgirl are symptoms of sexual alienation. Indeed, for them the playboy and playgirl life-styles constitute the more serious danger, since they arise out of the new technocratic order rather than some dying moral order, and since they appear as sexual liberation and fulfillment rather than as just another version of desensitization and repression.

At this point I should mention that most theorists of the Counterculture had completed their work before the emergence of such publications as *Playgirl* and *Viva* mazagines. They therefore tend to focus on the inadequacies of playboy sex, making little or no mention of its female counterpart. But I am sure that all the evils they impute to playboy sex they would also impute to playgirl sex.

The Countercultural movement's castigation of playboy sex is confronted immediately with the following objection. Since playboys are encouraged to engage in whatever sexual activity they please, and since they seem to have no inhibitions about any kind of sexual activity, then in what sense can they be called "repressed" or "unfree" or "alienated" from their bodies? And on what basis can it be claimed that the current forms of sexual promiscuity exemplified by playboy sex are generated by the institutionalization of technological rationality?

Countercultural Dystopians, and especially Herbert Marcuse and Theodore Rozsak, have been quick to point out the undesirable features of the current forms of sexual permissiveness. For example, playboy sex is the prerogative of the wealthy and the privileged and thus symptomizes the unjust stratifications and distributions of our socioeconomic system.

> In the affluent society, we have sex and sex galore—or so we are led to believe. But when we look more closely we see that this sybaritic promiscuity wears a special social coloring. It has been assimilated to an income level and social status available only to our well-heeled junior executives and the jet set. After all, what does it cost to rent these yachts full of nymphomaniacal young things in which our playboys sail off for orgiastic swimming parties in the Bahamas? *Real* sex, we are led to believe, is something that goes with the best scotch, twenty-seven dollar sun glasses, and platinum-tipped shoelaces. Anything less is a shabby substitute. Yes, there is permissiveness in the technocratic society; but it is only for the swingers and the big spenders.[1]

Playboy sex is obviously male chauvinist.

> The ideal of the swinging life we find in *Playboy* gives us a conception of femininity which is indistinguishable from social idiocy. The woman becomes a mere playmate, a submissive bunny, a mindless decoration. At a stroke, half the population is reduced to being the inconsequential entertainment of the technocracy's pampered elite.[2]

Though made more plentiful, sex is integrated into the system of production and exchange of commodities, thus becoming an important instrument for social control and manipulation.

It has often been noted that advanced industrial civilization operates with a greater degree of sexual freedom—"operates" in the sense that the latter becomes a market value and a factor of social mores. Without ceasing to be an instrument of labor, the body is allowed to exhibit its sexual features in the everyday work world and in work relations. This is one of the unique achievements of industrial society—rendered possible by the reduction of dirty and heavy physical labor; by the availability of cheap, attractive clothing, beauty culture, and physical hygiene. . . . The sexy office and salesgirls, the handsome, virile junior executive and floor-walker are highly marketable commodities. . . . Shops and offices open themselves through huge glass windows and expose their personnel; inside, high counters and nontransparent partitions are coming down. . . . Technical progress and more comfortable living permit the systematic inclusion of libidinal components into the realm of the commodity production and exchange.[3]

The officially sanctioned promiscuous sex is impersonal and detached.

Moreover, *Playboy* sexuality is, ideally, casual, frolicsome, and vastly promiscuous. It is the anonymous sex of the harem. It creates no binding loyalties, no personal attachments, no distractions from one's primary responsibilities. . . . The perfect playboy practices a career enveloped by noncommittal trivialities: there is no home, no family, no romance that divides the heart painfully. Life off the job exhausts itself in a constant run of imbecile affluence and impersonal orgasms.[4]

The increase in the availability of sex has been accompanied by a constriction of the bodily and environmental zones of pleasure. Whole sectors of the human environment and the human body have been deeroticized.

The environment from which the individual could obtain pleasure . . . has been rigidly reduced. . . . The effect is a localization and contraction of the libido, the reduction of erotic to sexual experience and satisfaction. For example, compare lovemaking in a meadow and in an automobile, on a lovers' walk outside the town walls and on a Manhattan street. In the former case, the environment partakes of and invites libidinal cathexis and tends to be eroticized. In contrast, a mechanized environment seems to block such self-transcendence of the libido.[5]

These observations, though apparently correct, are not altogether helpful. They may show that the playboy or his equivalent is immoral or asocial, but they do not necessarily establish that he is sexually repressed. If playboy sex is the preserve of the rich, if it is male chauvinist, and if it is used as an instrument for manipulation in commodity production and exchange, then it is obviously exploitative and unjust; and insofar as it reinforces detachment and uninvolvement, it is anticommunal. For these reasons and others, one can conclude that the playboy or any other beneficiary of the official sexual permissiveness is socially alienated. But it does not follow that he is sexually alienated. Is someone to be termed "sexually repressed" or "unsensuous" simply because he or she treats others as things or looks upon sex as a commodity? If so, then how can sexual alienation be distinguished from social alienation? In this context, isn't the expression "sexual alienation" totally superfluous?

It makes sense to say that the playboy is sexually repressed or alienated only if one is willing to claim that he misses out on some important types of sexual enjoyment. Of the five criticisms of his lifestyle quoted above, only the last explicitly makes this charge. Herbert Marcuse claims here that for the playboy much of the human body and much of the environment has been deeroticized. The playboy is not sensitive to the beauty of the natural environment or of the parts of the body which are not relevant to genital pleasure. Marcuse seems to assume that certain kinds of environment are intrinsically erotic (for example, a woodland setting) and some are intrinsically unerotic (such a playboy bachelor "pad"), and that the playboy is oblivious to these differences. But this seems wrong. Whether or not one's environment is erotic depends on one's taste and one's response to that environment. Even a parked car may be erotic for one who has a fetish for, say, the Cadillac Eldorado. And there is no doubt that the exemplary playboy will provide an environment suitable for his brand of lovemaking, and hence an environment which is in his eyes erotic. No doubt someone like Marcuse, or any other representative of the Counterculture, would be offended by *Playboy* publisher Hugh Hefner's mansion in Chicago. We may agree that Hefner has philistine taste, but still, perhaps like beauty, the erotic is in the eye of the beholder. What is for a participant of the Counterculture a desensitized environment may for the playboy be an erotically stimulating environment.

There is no doubt that playboy sex fixates in an exaggerated way on genital pleasure. This obviously does not mean that for the playboy the other parts of the human body and the environment are not erotic. It means that the other parts of the body and the environment are sources of sexual pleasure for the playboy only to the extent that they contribute to or pave the way for genital pleasure, and especially genital orgasm. If true, this is an inadequacy. It seems that other parts or contours of the body, other movements of the body, as well as many features of the environment, ought to be intrinsic sources of sensual pleasure, independent of their contribution to genital pleasure. And if the playboy fails to derive pleasure from sensory contact with these parts or contours or movements, in the absence of present or future genital stimulation, then he can be said to be missing some important kinds of sensuous enjoyment. He can thus be termed "sensuously alienated" or "desensitized"; one can say that he is "out of harmony" with his body. It is presumably this sort of sensuous enjoyment which sensitivity programs try to reawaken or recreate. Participants are encouraged to increase their tactile concentration on their bodily parts and movements by touching, slapping, and lifting them. And they are drawn into a number of tactile rituals with other persons, involving anything from toe touching and back rubbing to blind walking, head washing, palm dancing, and body lifting. No doubt, much of what is prescribed in these sessions is quackery. Still, the large demand for these programs is evidence of a need felt by many to acquire the capacity for sensuously enjoying, in a manner independent of genital sexuality, theirs and other persons' bodies. Insofar as the playboy is in need of such therapy, then he can be deemed sensuously repressed. This Countercultural critique of playboy sexuality, though persuasive and on the right track, is as it stands too weak and ill-defined. For the argument faults the playboy not for the sensuous activity which he does exhibit (genital sex), but for the sensuous activity which he does not exhibit. The playboy is criticized not for what he gets but for what he misses. But why couldn't the playboy be trained to add to his repertoire of pleasures those nongenital sensuous pleasures prescribed by the Countercultural humanist? Why couldn't he broaden his sensuous horizons by taking part in sensitivity sessions while keeping the remainder of his life-style intact? The Countercultural argument would be effective only if it established either that playboy genital sex is a distorted form of sensuality which inhibits the development of a capacity for nongenital sensuous enjoyment, or that the interpersonal lifestyles associated with playboy sex (such as casualness, uninvolvement, and male chauvinism) are incompatible with true sensuous fulfillment, whether of the genital or nongenital type. But the argument as it stands fails to establish either of these points. Thus, it fails to show that the playboy cannot remain a playboy and still participate fully in the nongenital sensuous enjoyments prescribed by the Counterculture.

The Countercultural critique of playboy sex, in its present form, is also vague and ill-defined. It shifts in focus from the idea of sexual repression, which is only a particular kind of sensuous repression, to the idea of sensuous repression as such, or desensitization. That is, it shifts from the narrow and fairly clear notion of genital sex to the much broader and more vague notion of sensuousness. The playboy is accused of missing nonsexual forms of sensuousness. But while the demarcation between sexual and nonsexual pleasure is fairly clear, the demarcation between sensuous and nonsensuous pleasure or activity is not so clear. What is to count as sensuous pleasure and what as nonsensuous pleasure? What is to count as the sensuous component in pleasure and what as the nonsensuous component? Sensuous enjoyment simply cannot be identified with tactile enjoyment. However sensuality is defined, it obviously involves gustatory, olfactory, visual, and auditory components. Are the pleasures generated by the discovery of a new theorem, the study of philosophy, the discovery of oil deposits, the making of an important sale, or the reading of a good book sensuous or not? If not sensuous, then what precisely do they lack?

According to spokespersons for the Counterculture, all or most of us brought up in a technocratic society are sensuously alienated or desensitized. This being the case, they cannot easily teach us the meaning of the term "sensuous" demonstratively by pointing to those of our experiences which are unqualifiedly sensuous; we probably have few undistorted sensuous experiences. "Sensuous" then is a theoretical term, which can only be defined indirectly, negatively, and analogically.

What then can the Counterculture mean by "sensuous alienation," "desensitization," "sensuous uptightness"? Perhaps we will get a clue if we find out what connection there is, according to spokespersons for the Counterculture, between the growing institutionalization of technological values (technological rationality) and the growth of the new forms of sensuous alienation associated with playboy sex.

Sensuous Repression: The Complete Technician

In what way does the institutionalization of technological rationality lead to desensitization? If the principles of technological rationality govern the processes of production, then they are most probably internalized by the population involved in production. This internalization may be so effective that it carries over into the leisure life of the working population. Desensitization may thus be a consequence of the fact that all the experience and activity of this population, either at or away from work, is interpreted exclusively in terms of, and governed exclusively by, the principles of technological rationality.

It is a common complaint against scientists and technicians that they allow the attitudes and mentalities which prevail in the laboratory or office to govern their personal and social lives. This is the point behind castigations of scientists and technicians for being "robots" or "computers." It is assumed that a scientist or technician, when acting in his or her capacity as scientist or technician, is not experiencing or performing in a sensuous manner. Thus a person who always experiences or performs as scientist or technician, even in contexts which are not appropriately scientific or technological, is deemed to be desensitized or sensuously repressed. For the Countercultural Dystopian, the paradigm case of the sensuously repressed individual is that of a person who behaves as a technician in wholly inappropriate contexts, such as sexual interaction, dance, music performance and composition, informal conversation, gymnastics, and interaction with wildlife.

This provides us with at least the basis for a negative elucidation of the Countercultural notion of the sensuous. Those forms of cognition, activities, and attitudes which are sensuous are most perspicuously describable in terms of their contrasts with forms of cognition, activities, and attitudes which are scientific and technological. Consider the following examples. For science and technology, sensory perception is simply a means or a starting point; it is essential that the functions of science and technology go beyond sensory perception, or what is given in sensory perception. Scientists use perception to aid in the discovery or confirmation of nonperceptual truths about the universe; they make theoretical claims which, among other things, explain away what is given in perception. Technologists use perceptual experience mainly in order to increase their manipulative power over nature, and particularly over the objects of sensory perception. In sensuous cognition, on the other hand, the sensory experience is an end in itself. It requires one's undivided attention. One simply savors the sensory experience without reference to any ulterior motives. Whether submitting oneself to psychedelic drugs or listening to music or participating in sensitivity sessions, the sensuous person is in a wholly receptive, rather than interpretative or manipulative, frame of mind.

Scientific and technological activity is reflective; sensuous activity is not. The technician typically subjects future projects to elaborate planning and careful deliberation and subjects past projects to detailed scrutiny. Sensuous experience or activity, on the other hand, is presumably "spontaneous," that is, it is not preceded by specific expectations or preparations, and cannot after its occurrence be subject to dissection and analysis. Thus, the playboy, in virtue of the fact that he involves himself in elaborate schemes for future seductions and elaborate reviews of past seductions, can be described as desensitized.

Science and technology are open-ended disciplines. There is always more to be learned about nature and more power over nature to be acquired; there are always more tasks to be done and more objectives to be reached. Therefore, scientists or technicians are essentially future oriented and are willing to engage constantly in routine or frustrating or exhausting work in order to achieve some future good. They are thus willing to forego present enjoyment for future enjoyment. In contrast, people involved in sensuous activity are completely absorbed in the pleasures of the moment, and are minimally inclined to postpone present gratification in order to achieve some future good.

One in a scientific or technical state of mind tends to atomize cognitions and behavior; one in a sensuous state of mind treats them as wholes which are irreducible to their component parts. A well-conceived research project or experiment is broken down into basic steps and stages, and into subtasks and subroutines. Scientific conjectures are similarly broken down into component claims which can be discretely and differentially tested. It is well known that the maximization of efficiency demands a continued microfractionalization of technical occupations. The Countercultural Dystopian assumes that it would be desensitizing to atomize in this way one's sexual experiences and activities, one's intimate interpersonal relations, one's dancing, and one's sensory enjoyment of nature.

One distinction continually made between science and technology, on the one hand, and true sensuousness, on the other, is that the former is dominated by "technique" (formal rules specifying the most efficient means for achieving given ends) in a way in which the latter is not. A major Dystopian complaint against modern "liberated" sex is that it has been completely "technized"; Dystopians point to the proliferation of "how to do it" books on sex which promise automatic success if certain techniques are followed or certain exercises are carried out. Our sensuous capacities presumably are blunted by this excessive preoccupation with technique. Of course, the successful performance of any sensuous activity, be it sex or dancing, requires some artfulness, and artfulness presupposes the implemenation of some techniques. And it is also true that most scientific and technological activities are not completely circumscribed by technical rules. Technical rules provide a complete decision procedure for arithmetical calculation and for the validation of mathematical proofs, but they fail to provide a complete decision procedure for the making of mathematical, scientific, or technological discoveries, or for the confirmation or disconfirmation of scientific hypotheses. Nevertheless, it could be claimed for the following reasons that technique has a much greater impact on scientific and technological consciousness than it does on sensuous consciousness. One learns science by being explicitly and systematically taught to follow technical rules. And the practicing scientist not only acts in accordance with technical rules, but is always in the process of formulating old and new rules and procedures, of consciously bringing these rules to bear in plans and deliberations, and of consciously assessing by reference to these rules. On the other hand, it is often claimed that the capacity for sensuous enjoyment is a natural rather than a learned capacity, and that, like the capacity to walk, it is developed and molded through the processes of physical maturation rather than through technical inculcation. The stress on the learning of techniques, it is assumed, would merely distract from these natural capacities and stunt their growth. Furthermore, though mature sensuous activity may conform with some technical rules, it is not preceded and accompanied by the continuous formulation and consideration of these rules and it is not assessed after the fact by the application of these rules. Presumably, the heavy emphasis on the consciousness of techniques, typical of science and technology, inhibits or distorts sensuous enjoyment.

The attitude of science and technology relative to its object of study is one of personal detachment and uninvolvement. In contrast, the attitude of sensuous cognition is essentially one of empathy for the object of knowledge; in sensuous awareness, cognition entails conation. This is not to say, however, that the scientist as scientist is dispassionate in the pursuit of professional goals. The ideal scientist surely has a strong passion for truth and beauty, and certainly is emotionally involved in the work at hand. Still, it is irrelevant to this work that there be a strong personal attachment on the part of the scientist to the coparticipants or the objects of the inquiries. Indeed, as is well known, such personal involvements, though allowed, jeopardize objectivity.

All scientific and technological knowledge is verbally expressible and when communicated is communicated verbally. According to Countercultural spokespersons, this is not true of many forms of sensuous cognition, such as psychedelic experience or intimate interpersonal experience. For example, one's intimate knowlege of a given person's face, it is assumed, cannot be fully expressed verbally. Furthermore, it is emphasized that sensuous communication is more effectively carried out through body movement, facial expression, touch, and music than it is through linguistic interchange. Finally, science is directed mainly at the knowledge of classes or types, whereas sensuous experience is directed at the knowledge of individuals.

The above, I think, is a fairly accurate reconstruction of the Counterculture's understanding of the contrasts between the way of life of the pure technician and that of the wholly sensuous person. From these contrasts the following conclusion can be drawn. Any person can be deemed wholly desensitized or sensuously repressed who, during all of both leisure and work time consistently experiences things or persons in a theoretical, manipulative, and detached state of mind, consistently subjects every action to careful planning and detailed atomization, is consistently inclined to postpone present gratification, consistently brings techniques to bear in everything learned or done, and consistently accentuates verbal (at the expense of nonverbal) cognition and communication. Consequently, anyone is desensitized who has internalized the principles of technological rationality in both leisure life and work life.

It is obvious that in any technologically advanced society, and especially in a technocracy, work activities and experiences will be imbued with the principles of technological rationality. But why should we expect the leisure experiences and activities of these same employees also to be dominated by the principles of technological rationality? Why couldn't the scientist or technician who behaves nonsensuously while on the job behave in a wildly sensuous manner while off the job (as many try to do)? The Dystopian's response to this objection would be straightforward and reasonable. In any full-employment economy, leisure is institutionally subordinated to work. Most of the workers' most precious hours and much of their concentration and energy are mobilized for their work. Most of their socialization, education, and training are directed toward the preparation for future employment; an important function of school is to inculcate work disciplines as well as to teach work skills. Only those forms of leisure life which are compatible with, or contribute to, maximum work productivity are tolerated or reinforced; and apparently, according to Countercultural Dystopians, persons who enjoyed a completely sensuous life would hardly be inclined to spend their most important waking hours at work. Hence, it is not surprising that, in a full-employment economy, the values internalized in one's work experience and activity should also be internalized in one's leisure experience and activity.

But why should we expect that in technocratic America, in an America dominated by modern technology, the economy will continue to be a full-employment economy? Shouldn't the emergence of a post-industrial era, involving as it does the spread of computer technology and automation, entail a constant reduction in the size of the work force and in the length of the work-year? In the long run, would it not entail the virtual elimination of human productive labor? Can Dystopians rationally deny this? Let us see on what basis they would.

Sensuous Repression: The Imperatives of Work

Countercultural Dystopians seem to agree on this point: postindustrial technocracies, as well as the industrial capitalist societies of old, are and will continue to be compulsively committed to maximal economic growth. They think that continued economic growth is one of the most important values embodied in technological rationality: the "good" of technology, they think, requires economic growth. There appear to be two reasons for this. Economic growth is necessary for the continued expansion of human collective power over nature and for the continued development of scientific and technological knowledge. But control over nature and growth in technology are the two most basic goals of institutionalized technology and of the decision-making technicians overseeing its development.

Wealth obviously is a form of power; one's wealth is measured by one's command over resources, goods, and services. It is reasonable to believe that continued growth in our collective power over nature presupposes continued growth in our collective wealth, this in turn being made possible by continued growth in the gross national product (GNP).

Furthermore, it could be argued with some plausibility that continued technological growth will require increasing demands for research and development funds, and that these demands on the community pool of investment funds can be met more easily in the face of competing demands from other interests by continually enlarging the available pool.

Thus a Dystopian might argue that for the foreseeable future economic growth will be required to meet the needs of modern technology. Though persuasive, the reasons need to be looked at more carefully; this will be done in chapter 9. Meanwhile, let us follow the Dystopian argument to its natural conclusion.

Even in an age of automation, the pursuit of economic growth is in conflict with the pursuit of leisure. Suppose that in a given year the modernization of machinery raises the hourly productivity of each worker by 5 percent. One option in response to this is to decrease the working time of each worker by 5 percent while providing the same income. This, however, disallows any increase in total production.

Another option is to increase total production by 5 percent by adding to the stock of machinery, but then any increase in leisure is disallowed.

Any growth economy presupposes the existence of scarcity, whether natural or contrived. Without scarcity, the worker will not ask for more work and the consumer for more goods. It has been argued by Dystopians (and most perceptively by Philip Slater) that sex, as the object of a primary human need and as the only source of gratification which is plentiful in the "hypothetical state of nature," must be made artificially scarce in societies committed to sustained economic growth. How this is accomplished depends on the relative wealth of the society in question. In poor countries with a shortage of savings and capital, the emphasis is on frugality and self-denial; sexual scarcity is generated by the imposition of restrictions or taboos on sex with respect to time, place, manner, and person. In more opulent countries where savings tend to be overabundant, the emphasis is rather on self-indulgence and consumption. Sexual scarcity is bred in these permissive societies, not by imposing restrictions, but by so integrating sex in the system of compulsive commodity consumption that no finite amount of sexual indulgence can ever satisfy one's sexual needs. Inanimate commodities (such as soaps and cars) and animate "commodities" (such as Playmates and fashion models and stripteasers), as well as certain forms of dress and communicative behavior, are imbued with a sexual significance they cannot possibly fulfill. Philip Slater makes this point fairly nicely.

> Thus, while increases in the number, variety, and severity of sexual restrictions may intensify the subjective experiences of sexual scarcity, a subsequent trend toward sexual "permissiveness" need not produce a corresponding decrease in scarcity. . . . The fundamental mechanism for generating sexual scarcity is to attach sexual interest to inaccessible, nonexistent, or irrelevant objects. . . . Today this basic technique has become the dominant one. By the time an American boy or girl reaches maturity he or she has so much symbolic baggage attached to the sexual impulse that the mere mutual stimulation of two human bodies seems almost meaningless. Through the mass media everything sexless has become sexualized: automobiles, cigarettes, detergents, clothing.[6]

In conclusion, it would seem that the imperatives of technology require maximal economic growth. This in turn entails full employment and compulsive consumption. Full employment presupposes that work is at the center of each person's life; it presupposes that each person internalizes the perspectives of work and is willing to postpone gratification. In an advanced technological full-employment economy, the worker will internalize the technical point of view (the principles of technological rationality) in leisure life as well as work life. For all these reasons, workers in advanced technological societies will tend to be desensitized. Desensitization is further instilled by the requirements of compulsive consumption. Compulsive consumption exists when the wants of consumers grow faster than the stock of goods and services or when existing wants cannot be satisfied by any amount of goods and services. Compulsive consumerism requires contrived scarcity within a context of abundance, and this in sexual matters as well as others. Insofar as playboy sex is "technical sex," fashioned by the experiences of technical work, and insofar as it presupposes or instills sexual scarcity within a context of abundant sex, then it is by the standards of the Counterculture a form of desensitized or repressed sex.

So goes the Dystopian argument. It purports to show that playboy sex is a natural concommitant of advanced technological societies and that it is a form of desensitized sex. This argument, I think, is stimulating and interesting. Whether it works depends on some key assumptions which have to be investigated later (like the assumption that advanced technological societies are necessarily committed to maximum growth).

Some Difficulties

Not all members of the Counterculture are Dystopians; that is, not all hold technology primarily responsible for sexual alienation. Dystopians are somewhat ambivalent themselves, and quite rightly so. It is difficult to see how the Countercultural ideal of sexual liberation could be met anywhere but in a highly sophisticated technological society. Proponents of the Counterculture tell us that widespread leisure is an indispensable condition of sexual liberation. Though they call us back to a simple life away from the pressures of compulsive consumption, they propound a life-style which presupposes the availability of many modern goods and services, such as a developed system of education, universal medical care, and universal accessibility to the arts, electronics, modern chemicals, and mass transportation. It is difficult to see how widespread leisure could be compatibly generated with the production of all these goods and services without the presence of a highly developed technology. There thus appears to be something incoherent in the Countercultural Dystopians' perspective. The ideal of sexual liberation seems both to presuppose modern technology and yet to be incompatible with it; the ideal, which they claim can be fulfilled, seems unfulfillable. Perhaps this indicates that their analysis of the causes of modern sexual alienation is mistaken. This is at least what Socialists would claim. Sexual alienation, they would argue, is due more to the imperatives of capitalism than to the imperatives of technology. In the following chapters, we will encounter again this running disagreement between Countercultural Dystopians and Socialists.

Notes

[1]Theodore Roszak, *The Making of a Counter-Culture* (Garden City: Doubleday, 1969), pp. 14–15.
[2]Ibid., p. 15.
[3]Herbert Marcuse, *One Dimensional Man* (Boston: Beacon, 1964).
[4]Roszak, *The Making of a Counter-Culture*, p. 15.
[5]Marcuse, *One Dimensional Man*, p. 73.
[6]Philip Slater, *The Pursuit of Loneliness* (Boston: Beacon, 1970), p. 85.

8

Alienated Labor

There is little doubt that many working Americans are alienated from their work, but it is not so easy to tell what causes this alienation. Dystopians primarily blame technology and predict that alienation will intensify as technology continues to grow.

This claim (that alienation of work grows as technology grows) constitutes perhaps the most powerful and persuasive case put forth by Dystopians against modern technology. Certainly it is more plausible than their claim that sexual alienation grows as technology grows. Utopians might justifiably wave aside the Dystopian complaints about sexual alienation, but they cannot ignore the Dystopian complaints about the alienation of work. On this issue the Dystopians certainly have the initiative. The best way to test the adequacy of the Dystopians' position on the issue of work alienation is to see how Utopians could respond to their charge that modern technology is the primary cause of work alienation. The burden of rebuttal certainly seems to be on the shoulders of Utopians.

Utopians must respond that alienation in work is decreasing and will continue to decrease as modern technology develops. Can they do this successfully? Robert Blauner in *Alienation and Freedom* has certainly made a good try.[1] He concedes (as it appears he must) that the alienation of workers increased dramatically during the era of industrial technology. But he argues that in the eras of postindustrial technology and (specifically) automation, alienation of work is decreasing and will continue to do so as technology grows. Blauner's strategy in dealing with Dystopian criticisms is the standard Utopian strategy: concede that industrial technology has had bad effects, but argue that postindustrial technology will on the whole have good effects.

In the following sections I will reconstruct, by making use of Blauner's and others' critiques, the Utopian response to the Dystopian charges about technology and alienated labor; I will evaluate them and attempt to see whether they are successful in rebutting the Dystopian charges.

Alienated Labor: The Industrial Era

First, something must be said about the nature of work and the meaning of the alienation of work.

Work can be distinguished from leisure in the following way: work is any activity whose function it is to provide socially necessary or desirable goods and services for oneself or others. Providing food, manufacturing clothing, and repairing household appliances are all work activities; collecting stamps and playing solitaire are leisure activities. Playing pick-up basketball on weekends is a leisure activity; playing professional basketball is work.

Work is rarely wholly pleasant and free. That is why it must usually be remunerated. Work has been found bad or unpleasant for a variety of reasons: it is too time-consuming; it is fatiguing and exhausting; it is boring and repetitious; it is subject to external control and supervision; it is unhealthy and dangerous; it gives little meaning to one's life. Not all kinds of work exhibit all of these bad traits, and a few kinds of work exhibit none of them.

To say that a kind of work is alienating is to say that it has some bad or unpleasant traits, but to say of some kind of work that it has bad or unpleasant traits does not entail that it is alienating. The word "alienation" is only used to refer to a subset of bad or unpleasant features of work, not to all such bad or unpleasant features. In this sense, work that is fatiguing may not be alienating. What bad things about work does the word "alienation" refer to?

Robert Blauner, following other sociologists, characterizes the alienation of work in the following manner. According to him, workers are alienated to the extent that they are powerless in carrying out their work (i.e., they have no control over the quantity, quality, direction, and pace of the work); or to the extent that their work is meaningless (i.e., it has no clear relation to a broader life program or production program); or to the extent that they are self-estranged (i.e., they do not identify with their work or enjoy it or find it challenging); or to the extent that they are socially isolated from their superiors or coworkers.[2]

For example, the powerlessness of workers increases if their movements are increasingly paced by machines or if they are increasingly subject to closer supervision and regulation. Their work becomes more meaningless as it is increasingly subdivided into minute tasks each of which is carried out by different workers. Consider the case of nineteenth-century needle workers, each of whom performed only one of the twenty tasks involved in the making and packaging of needles. Some spent the whole day drawing wire, some straightening it, some pointing it, while others twisted and cut the heads. No doubt the work of the needle workers was in this respect meaningless as is the work of contemporary assembly line workers. Workers become more self-estranged in their work when it becomes more repetitious, boring, and unskilled. There is usually a correlation between increasing meaninglessness and increasing self-estrangement of work. Workers become more socially isolated as their relations with each other and with their bosses become more impersonal and formalized, and as they work more by themselves and less in cooperation with others.

The industrial era may have improved the lot of workers in many ways; remuneration may have become higher and gross fatigue lower (though this is not sure). Some of the bad or unpleasant features of work may have been attenuated in the industrial era, at least by the time that it ran its course. But there can be no doubt that the rise of industrial technology in the West has been associated with increasing powerlessness, meaninglessness, self-estrangement, and social isolation for the worker, and hence with dramatic increases in the alienation of the worker. This the Utopian must concede.

Preindustrial manufacture was carried out by skilled artisans and their apprentices. Their work was varied and highly challenging. It took many years to learn, and they could conduct it at their own pace to produce commodities that suited their own creative taste. In a nutshell, preindustrial artisans had considerable power over their work and its product. They identified with their work and found it meaningful and they performed it in cooperation with others. They were therefore relatively unalienated in their work. With the industrial revolution in the West, the conditions of work changed dramatically. In came the large factory system with its bureaucratic and hierarchic social structure. In came job standardization, job specialization, and the extreme subdivision of tasks. In came mechanization, with the transfer of skills from workers to machines. As the industrial era matured, the lot of the worker began in some respects to improve: wages went up, the workday was shortened, fringe benefits were introduced, and health conditions were improved. Nonetheless, alienation was still on the increase. Modern assembly line workers in Detroit may be economically better off than their forebears in textile mills. But, Robert Blauner argues, they are significantly more alienated than their forebears in textile firms. The work of assembly line operatives is much more rigidly controlled by machines than that of nineteenth-century textile operatives; it is less skilled, much more subdivided, and significantly more isolated socially. Indeed, today, workers on automobile assembly lines have become everyone's favorite examples of alienated workers. They are continual subjects of television documentaries, interviews, and sociology research projects. They articulate most vividly the conditions of alienated work:

> The job gets so sickening—day in and day out plugging in ignition wires. I get through with one motor, turn around and there's another motor staring me in the face. It's sickening.
>
> The assembly line is no place to work, I can tell you. There is nothing more discouraging than having a barrel with another 10,000 bolts in it and using them all up. Then you get a barrel with another 10,000 bolts, and you know every one of these 10,000 bolts has to be picked up and put in exactly the same place as the last 10,000 bolts.[3]

The alienation of work became a serious problem during the period of industrial technology in the West. The industrial revolution brought about a marked increase in work alienation; it replaced the artisan with the machine operator. The slow transition from nineteenth-century sweatshops to the modern antiseptic and highly rationalized industrial plants only served to intensify this alienation.

Faced with this conclusion, Utopians, as the defenders of technology against Dystopian charges, have only one option. They can concede that alienated labor is a necessary consequence of industrial technology. But they can respond (as Blauner does) that we are moving from the industrial to the postindustrial age in technology, and that in the postindustrial age technological innovation will reverse the trend toward greater alienation in work. Postindustrial technology, they can argue, will bring about significant decreases in the alienation of work.

But how can postindustrial technology do for the workers what industrial technology could not? Here there are three possibilities. Postindustrial technology can greatly reduce the alienation of blue collar or manual laborers by ultimately bringing about the virtual elimination of all work, manual labor, or the alienating aspects of manual or blue-collar labor. If any of these answers is convincing, then Utopians can successfully rebut the Dystopian charges that modern technology (whether industrial or postindustrial) will continue to maintain, or even intensify, the alienation of workers.

The Elimination of Work

Is it rational to believe that work will slowly but inevitably be eliminated in postindustrial America? Are we moving toward a leisure society? Will the amount of work performed by each human decrease as postindustrial technology develops?

Despite what Utopians may tell us, there is no good reason to believe that technological growth and increase in leisure are positively correlated. In the last chapter, I cited a speculative Dystopian argument purporting to show that continued technological growth presupposes a full-employment economy. This conclusion may be a bit strong. Yet, there is evidence to back up the weaker conclusion that technological growth (whether postindustrial or other) does not of itself decrease the amount of work hours which each human must contribute. As is well known, there is no general correlation between increases in productivity and long-term increases in unemployment. Even studies of individual industries show that the rate of change in productivity and the rate of change in unemployment have little in common. Changes in employment seem to depend much more on the changing demand for goods and services than any other factor.[4]

But if technological growth does not by itself generate long-term

increases in unemployment, doesn't it consistently generate more leisure time for employed persons in the form of a shorter workweek or of
a later entry into, or earlier exit from, the work force?

If one looks at long-range trends, it is again very difficult to find
any systematic correlation between technological growth and increases
in leisure time. In the preindustrial Western world, there appears to
have been a general trend toward increased leisure for nonagricultural
workers which peaked in the thirteenth century. By the thirteenth
century, urban artisans could count on as many as 171 days off, mostly
in the form of holy days; they worked approximately 2,300 hours per
year. But after the thirteenth century a reverse trend set in. As Europe
began moving toward the industrial revolution, the number of working
hours per day began to increase and the number of holy days to decrease. By the end of the eighteenth century, many day laborers were
at work between fourteen and eighteen hours per day, and very few
worked less than twelve hours a day (six days a week); day laborers
commonly worked near 4,000 hours per year. Since the middle of the
nineteenth century, there has been a downward trend again. Today,
the manual laborer spends between 1,900 and 2,500 hours per year on
the job; in terms of leisure, the industrial (or postindustrial) manual
laborer has finally caught up with the medieval guildsman. However,
professionals and civil servants work considerably more than this,
somewhere between 3,000 and 3,500 hours per year.[5]

If we look at the history of the West, there is no constant correlation between technological growth and growth in leisure; sometimes
the former is associated with growth in leisure, and sometimes with
diminution in leisure. No doubt, the growth of leisure and technology
have been positively correlated in this century. But the rate of decrease of work time has not been terribly large (something like 4 percent every decade for the first half of this century); at this rate, it would
take near two hundred years to cut in half our present workweek or
workyear. Because of the increase in life expectancy, the number of
years each adult human can expect to work has increased since 1900.
And in the last fifteen years, increases in leisure for manual workers
and others have been very small or nonexistent.[6]

Furthermore, much of these recent niggardly gains in leisure have
been gains in "forced leisure" or "false leisure." Manual workers find

their new leisure too often in the form of forced unemployment, layoffs, or part-time jobs. A good number of workers "moonlight" during their free time. Furthermore, much of the new free time is devoted to the increasingly complex duties of household management (such as food shopping, caring for appliances and automobiles, paying off bills, filling out tax forms). And commuting usually requires more time than it once did.

There does not seem, therefore, much reason to hope that work will be eliminated in the foreseeable future as a consequence of the impact of postindustrial technology. It does not appear, at this time, that postindustrial technology will solve the problem of alienated work in the foreseeable future by greatly reducing the amount of work that humans have to perform.

The Elimination of Manual Labor

If postindustrial technology is not bringing about the elimination of work in general, perhaps it is bringing about the elimination of manual work. So such Utopians as Daniel Bell have argued. But this tack simply will not work, for reasons given below.

Social scientists usually divide the work force into four categories—the white-collar worker, the blue-collar worker, the service worker, and the farm worker. They have gone out of their way to show that the number of farm workers and blue-collar workers have been declining proportionately relative to the number of white-collar and service workers. For example, between 1947 and 1965, the proportion of blue-collar workers in the work force went down from 41 percent to 37 percent, whereas the proportion of white-collar workers went up from 35 percent to 45 percent, and the proportion of service workers from 10 percent to 13 percent. By 1965, white-collar workers had replaced blue-collar workers as the most populous group in the work force. [7] These facts could easily lead a Utopian to conclude that in the postindustrial world the blue-collar worker will gradually disappear from the work force and, hence, that manual work, and with it the alienation of work, will gradually disappear. But this conclusion would be confused in many ways.

First, the fact that the proportion of blue-collar workers is dwindling does not necessarily mean that the absolute number of blue-collar workers is dwindling. Indeed, the opposite has been the case; the number of blue-collar workers has been increasing, and sometimes at comparatively high rates.[8] Changes in the proportionate composition of the work force, too, seem to have slowed somewhat.

Second, it is a confusion to identify the class of blue-collar workers (the so-called production workers) with the class of manual laborers. Though all blue-collar workers are manual laborers, not all manual laborers are blue-collar workers. Many manual laborers belong to the white-collar and service groups. For example, to the category of service workers belong garbage collectors, waiters, domestics, elevator operators, police officers, cooks, and gas station operators; the category of white collar workers includes mail carriers, mimeograph operators, cashiers, supermarket employees, typists, and telephone operators. Certainly these service and white-collar workers have more in common with the manual workers of the blue-collar force than the intellectual and nonmanual professional workers (such as accountants, lawyers, teachers) of the white-collar force.[9] And surely these manual workers in the service and white-collar categories are just as vulnerable to the prospects for alienation as the manual workers in the blue-collar category. Indeed, studies have shown that lower-level office workers exhibit as much, and the same kind of, alienation as do blue-collar workers once their workplace has been appropriately mechanized. The only difference in this respect between blue-collar manual workers and service manual workers is that the latter are only in the primitive stages of mechanization and have not yet reached the highest peaks of alienation.[10]

If all manual workers other than farm workers were regrouped under one category, they would easily constitute a majority of the work force. Under this new grouping, 60 to 62 percent of all workers would be classified as manual laborers.[11]

Consequently, it seems wrong to conclude as some Utopians do that the proportion and number of manual workers is dwindling as the new technology is growing. Given the present trends, we cannot expect that postindustrial technology, in the foreseeable future, will eliminate work alienation by eliminating the manual labor force.

The Elimination of Alienation

If we can discern no significant trend in postindustrial America toward the elimination of work in general or manual work in particular, then there remains only one possible way for the new postindustrial technology to eliminate or significantly decrease the alienation of work. This would be by so transforming the conditions of manual labor that the amount of alienation involved in manual work is greatly reduced. Can Utopians reasonably argue that the revolution brought about in the workplace by postindustrial technology will be significant enough to cancel out all the increases in alienation brought about by the revolution in the work place previously caused by industrial technology? Robert Blauner makes an interesting try at it.

He starts with the claim that work conditions have been just as radically transformed by the postindustrial revolution as they were by the industrial revolution. While the industrial revolution brought about the transition from crafts production to mechanized production, the postindustrial revolution is bringing about the transition from mechanized to automated production. According to him, automated production differs as much from mechanized production as mechanized production differed from crafts production. As the industrial revolution replaced the worker as artisan by the worker as machine operator, the postindustrial revolution is replacing the worker as machine operator by the worker as machine monitor.[12]

At the level of mechanized production (as we saw in chapter 3) machines provide the power for production and do either the materials processing or the materials handling. In textile production, for example, humans do the materials handling (for instance, transfer materials from one production stage to another) while the machines (say, the looms) do the materials processing (changing yarn into cloth). In automobile production, humans do the materials processing with tools, while the conveyer belt does the materials handling. In all types of mechanization some humans perform the control procedures; they gather information continually about the state of production, process that information, and then execute commands for appropriate changes in the quality, quantity, or pace of production. In automation, machines do both the materials processing and the materials handling, and, equipped with sensory devices, data processing capacities, and feedback loops they carry out most of the control procedures.[13]

Automation has so far been most easy to implement in continuous processing firms (such as oil and chemical firms) whose materials of production can easily flow from one stage to another. The workers in these firms contribute mainly to the control procedures of the machines by observing dials and gauges, taking readings of temperature and pressure, turning valves, and doing maintenance work when there is a breakdown.

Blauner argues that typical workers in automated plants are much less alienated than their counterparts in mechanized plants. The former have considerable control over the pace and sequence of their work; they are even able to determine when and where to take their coffee breaks. They perform a number of different tasks, and in the process are able to roam all over the plant. They thus have a clear sense of the whole system of work and how their job fits into it. Each works as a member of a small team and the success of the whole team depends very much on the success of individual tasks. Their work generally requires more skill than that of laborers in mechanized plants, and they are subject to less supervision.[14]

There is reason to believe, then, that with the advent of automation, the powerlessness, meaninglessness, self-estrangement, and social isolation (in short, the alienation) of work will decline somewhat. The question is whether it will decline significantly. Perhaps the more sentimental among us will find the work of machine monitors, as described, much less interesting or appealing than that of old-fashioned artisans. For example, though machine monitors control the pace and sequence of their work, they do not control the pace and sequence of production. Though they understand the overall organization of work in their plants, they have little or no understanding of the production processes themselves. They have no direct sensory experience of the production processes; all they see are gauges and valves. Both the type of work they do and the type of output they produce are rigidly standardized; they have few opportunities for the expression of individuality. They of course determine the times when they make their rounds or have their coffee breaks; but this by itself cannot be terribly gratifying. Given the expensive and sophisticated machinery, the workers are burdened with fairly heavy responsibilities.[15] Though not closely supervised, they work under intense pressure, especially when there is a breakdown in operations. Thus there is reason to believe that there remains a considerable amount of alienation among workers in automated plants, though perhaps not so great as the alienation of workers in mechanized plants.

But even if it eliminated or significantly reduced the alienation of work, automation still will not provide for the foreseeable future a universal solution to the problem of alienation; for it is not spreading quickly enough to the rest of the economy. As of 1968, only between 1 and 2 percent of all workers were employed by firms (such as in the oil and chemicals industries) at the advanced stages of automation, and less than 20 percent were employed by firms which were at least moving toward automation (such as in the banking, telephone, rubber, and motor vehicles industries). Close to 40 percent of all workers were employed by firms (such as apparel, construction, retail) which are only in the beginning stages of mechanization. Generally, the rate of movement toward automation seems to have subsided somewhat in the past twenty years.[16]

There is good reason to believe that automation will not undo by itself all the forms of alienation which have been caused or intensified by mechanization. This means that the postindustrial era in technology by itself will most probably not be able to cancel out within the foreseeable future all the forms of alienation which have been associated with the industrial era in the West. It most probably will not eliminate work in general or manual work in particular, and it most probably will not significantly reduce all by itself the alienation of those who perform manual labor. This conclusion is a crushing blow to the Utopian position, and correspondingly strengthens the Dystopian position. However, Dystopians now have to counter the Marxist account of work alienation, which is somewhat more challenging.

Is Technology Really the Cause of Alienated Work?

Dystopians seem correct in predicting that continued technological growth in contemporary America will do little to alleviate alienation from work. But are .hey correct in blaming modern technology primarily for this continued or intensified alienation? Socialists also predict that alienation from work will either remain constant or grow in America as long as the socioeconomic system remains as it is. But they blame capitalism and not technology, or rather, they blame the capitalist uses of technology. In opposition to the Dystopians, Socialists say that modern technology, were it controlled by workers in a socialist society, would not make work alienated. The Dystopians of course maintain that wherever modern industrial or postindustrial technology exists, whether in capitalist, socialist, or technocratic societies, there will be significant alienation from work. Who is right, or at least closer to the truth? It is quite difficult to tell.

In fairness to the Socialist position, however, we must distinguish between technology and its applications. Technology is a kind of practical knowledge which at a given time can be applied in a number of ways. Take the case again of the nineteenth-century needle makers. The analysis of the process of needle making into twenty or so separate stages and the discovery that considerable time is saved if each stage is divided up among the workers are great advances in organizational technology. But these advances can be applied in a number of ways. One application is to get each worker always to work at the same stage, always to do the same thing. Another is to rotate the jobs around, so that a worker spends a few hours drawing the wire, a few hours straightening it, and a few hours packaging the final product. The second alternative seems considerably less alienating, but the capitalists picked the first alternative. Why?

Examples of this abound. Given present technology, there are a number of ways to produce a car. One is the assembly line approach where each worker performs the same small operation on each of the fifty or so cars that passes each hour. The other is the team approach where a small group of workers produce a car from scratch, and rotate jobs from shift to shift. Most capitalists have picked the first alternative. Again the question, why?

In the production process, capitalists have long decided to separate completely mental work from physical work, planning from execution. One group of workers (the "experts" and engineers) do the thinking and planning, another group (the manual laborers) do the executing with little or no thinking. But why shouldn't the workers have been given the knowledge and initiative to innovate, to improve, to plan, and to control what they do? Our technology is not so recondite that the workers could not share in it.

The answer to those questions might seem obvious: the capitalists' way was more "efficient." It was more efficient to commit workers to lifelong fractionalized jobs, doing the same thing from day to day. But efficiency is a relative thing. What counts as efficient depends on what goals we have. If the goal is to make people happy, to make them feel human, to make them as psychologically healthy as possible, then clearly the capitalists' way has not been the most efficient. If the goal is to increase profits, then the capitalists' way may have been the most efficient. In part, it appears that production technology has been applied in the way that it has in order to better control and discipline large armies of workers. Workers seem the more easily controlled if they always do the same simple task and if they have little or no productive knowledge.[17]

Depending on one's objectives, there are many possible efficient applications of a state of technology. The technology cannot be responsible for its applications because it is not responsible for the objectives or final goals that people have. It is the people who control the technology who are responsible, or so Socialists would argue.

Dystopians might respond that we have lost control over the applications of technology, that technology has gotten out of hand and now automatically generates its own applications. This is the theme of "runaway" technology which I shall examine in the next chapter.

Notes

[1]Robert Blauner, *Alienation and Freedom* (Chicago: University of Chicago Press, 1964).
[2]Ibid., pp. 15–34.
[3]Ibid., p. 117.
[4]Abram J. Jaffee and Joseph Froomkin, *Technology and Jobs* (New York: Praeger, 1968), pp. 65–69.
[5]Harold L. Wilensky, "The Uneven Distribution of Leisure: The Impact of Economic Growth on 'Free Time,' " in *Social Problems*, 9 (1961), 33–35.
[6]Ibid., pp. 36–37; National Commission on Technology, Automation, and Economic Progress, *Technology and the American Economy*, Vol. 1 (Washington, D.C.: Government Printing Office, 1966), p. 109.

[7]William Faunce, *Problems of an Industrial Society* (New York: McGraw-Hill, 1968), p. 56.

[8]Jaffe and Froomkin, *Technology and Jobs*, p. 83.

[9]Andrew Levison, *The Working Class Majority* (New York: Coward, McCann, and Geoghegan, 1974), pp. 22–23.

[10]Jon M. Shepard, *The Impact of Mechanization and Automation on Alienation in the Factory and the Office* (Springfield, Va.: Clearinghouse for Federal Scientific and Technical Information, 1970).

[11]Levison, *Working Class Majority*, pp. 25–29.

[12]Blauner, *Alienation and Freedom*, pp. 124–164.

[13]Cf. chapter 3, pp. 34–35.

[14]Blauner, *Alienation and Freedom*, pp. 124–164.

[15]Ibid.

[16]Faunce, *Problems*, pp. 53–55.

[17]Harry Braverman, *Labor and Monopoly Capital* (New York: Monthly Review, 1974).

9

Runaway Technology

Technological Fetishism

Self-alienation takes the form not only of alienation from one's activity (such as sex and work) but also of alienation from the product of one's activity (such as commodities and institutions). The latter happens when one loses control of or becomes subservient to the product of one's activity. In this sense of alienation, many Dystopians believe that we have become alienated from our technology. This is the view which I shall refer to as "technological fetishism."

Many people maintain that we have lost control over our technology. Indeed, they argue, though technology is merely a product of our activity, it has not only become independent of us its producers, but has actually become our master. Technology is running wild. It is like a machine out of control which is terrorizing everybody. It dominates us rather than we it. We are helpless in the face of its development and are forced to accept whatever impact it has on us.

This certainly expresses a fetishistic view about technology. To view something as a fetish is to view it as having certain mysterious and dark powers. A fetish is usually something made by humans (such as a talisman or an idol) which is thought in some way to rule over them. Of course, most fetishism is superstitious, but it need not be. That we should be able to create some mechanical monster (something not unlike Frankenstein's monster) which gets out of control and ravages us is certainly not beyond the range of technical possibility. And certainly many nonsuperstitious and otherwise intelligent people are technological fetishists, that is, they view technology as a fetish.

Philip Slater in his perceptive *The Pursuit of Loneliness*, provides us with a clear and eloquent expression of technological fetishism.

> While we think of ourselves as a people of change and progress, masters of our environment and our fate, we are no more entitled to this designation than the most superstitious savage, for our relation to change is wholly passive. We poke our noses out the door each day and wonder breathlessly what new disruptions technology has in store for us. We talk of technology as the servant of man, but it is a servant that now dominates the household, too powerful to fire, upon whom everyone is helplessly dependent. We tiptoe about and speculate about his mood. What will be the effects of such-and-such an invention? How will it change our daily lives? We never ask, do we want this, is it worth it? . . . We simply say "You can't stop progress" and shuffle back inside.[1]

This theme has been developed and defended in most detail and with the greatest single-mindedness by Jacques Ellul in his *Technological Society*.

To the sophisticated and academically trained reader, the thesis of technological fetishism may appear to be wholly bizarre and implausible, the product of a confused mind. It may appear untestable or not worthy of being tested. That technology has a life of its own, that it can become free of us or even dominate us, may seem just another anthropomorphic delusion which has been pandered to by the mass media.

This response, I think, is unfair. Technological fetishism can be formulated in a way which is clear and testable, though it usually is not. And it is not a wildly implausible view, though it is most probably false. In the ensuing sections, I will develop an interpretation of technological fetishism which is clear and testable, and then I will determine by the application of some tests whether it appears true or not. Other than providing illustrative quotes from the work of Jacques Ellul, I will spend relatively little time summarizing the generally obscure and confusing literature of technological fetishism.

Technology the Master?

What could it mean to say that technology is running wild, and that it has become our master and we its slaves? Part of what technological

fetishism seems to be saying is that, in the modern world, major transformations in technology bring about major transformations in politics,
economics, culture, and ethics; that is, it seems to be saying that the
imperatives of modern technology determine the structure of our political and economic systems, and the admissable range of life-styles and
ethical codes. It denies correspondingly that major transformations in
politics, economics, culture, and ethics have a significant impact on
technology. As Jacques Ellul puts it:

> We have already seen that, at the present, neither economic or political
> evolution conditions technical progress. Its progress is likewise indepen-
> dent of the social situation. The converse is actually the
> case. . . . Technique elicits and conditions social, political, and economic
> change. It is the prime mover of all the rest, in spite of any appearance to
> the contrary and in spite of human pride, which pretends that man's
> philosophical theories are still the determining influence and man's polit-
> ical regimes decisive factors in technical evolution.[2]

This, however, cannot be all that technological fetishism says. For the
claim that major transformations in technology bring about all other
kinds of major social transformations does not establish by itself that
technology is our master. For we, or some of us, may have chosen and
explicitly given direction to those major technological transformations
which have had such an impact on the social order; the consequent
transformations in politics, economics, culture, and moral values could
have been brought about ultimately as a consequence of our own
choices and plans. It is normal that even our more trivial decisions
considerably restrict our future options. If I travel by plane or live in
the country, I cannot do some of the things I can do if I travel by car or
live in the city. If I become a corporate executive, I can hardly take on
the life-style of a bohemian or a college professor. But it does not
follow, though conceivable, that I am a slave to the plane, the country,
or the corporation; it all depends on the extent to which I have freely
chosen to live in the country, travel by plane, or become a corporate
executive. Similarly, from the fact that technology determines many of
our political and cultural forms, it does not follow that technology is our
master; we might well have freely chosen the technological innovations
and applications which determine the form of our politics and culture.

Clearly, we cannot claim that technology is our master unless we can prove that it has a life of its own; that is, unless we can prove that humans really have no free choice over whether technology grows or how it grows. So technological fetishism involves a commitment not only to the moderate thesis that technology is the primary cause of social change, but also to the more radical thesis that the pace and direction of change in technology is inexorable, autonomous, and independent of rational and "free" human choice.

Ellul seems clearly committed to the second thesis:

> At the present time, technique has arrived at such a point in its evolution that it is being transformed and is progressing without decisive intervention by man.[3]

Indeed, he goes so far as to say:

> Technique, as I believe I have shown, is totally irrelevant to this notion and pursues no end, professed or unprofessed. It evolves in a purely causal way: the combination of preceding elements furnishes the new technical elements. There is no purpose or plan that is being progressively realized. There is not even a tendency toward human ends.[4]

On what basis does Ellul draw the surprising conclusion that technology grows independently of human choices, purposes, and actions? It is not clear. But, among other things, he seems to be appealing to the known fact that research and development (R&D), as presently constituted, exhibits sustained and irreversible growth. Discoveries and innovations lead to or generate further discoveries and innovations. The development of railroads led to improvements in bridge technology; the introduction of steel rails stimulated the development of high-speed trains, which in turn stimulated the development of air brakes. In electronics, vacuum tubes were followed by transistors, which were followed by micromodular components. Ellul interprets this phenomenon thusly:

> The first of these laws—and we base our conviction on the whole of history—makes us certain that every invention calls forth other technical inventions in other domains. There is never any question of the arrest of the process, and even less of backward movement. . . . What is it that determines this progression today? . . . Essentially, the preceding technical situation alone is determinative. When a given technical discovery occurs, it has followed almost of necessity certain other discoveries.

Human intervention in this succession appears only as an incidental cause, and no man can do this by himself. But anyone who is sufficiently up-to-date technically can make a valid discovery which rationally follows its predecessors and rationally heralds what is to follow.[5]

But here one must be very careful. From the fact that growth in R&D is sustained and irreversible, it does not follow (as Ellul seems to think) that it is autonomous. Even if it were autonomous, it would not follow (again as Ellul seems to think) that it was independent of rational human choice. A new discovery or invention paves the way for other discoveries or inventions in the sense that it makes these discoveries or inventions more feasible and probable. But this new capacity does not translate into a new actuality all by itself; some human intervention is obviously required, as even Ellul admits. The question has to do with the nature of this human intervention and the conditions under which it takes place. Whether or not R&D growth is autonomous and whether or not it is independent of rational human choice depends on the manner in which human intervention is brought about. For example, humans may only support and pursue R&D as a means to achieve some nontechnological goal, such as military superiority or economic growth. If such is the case, then R&D growth, though sustained and irreversible, is obviously not autonomous or independent of human rational choice; it is being generated and directed by some external human goal and is at the service of other human institutions or endeavors. However, if R&D is supported and pursued as an end in itself or in order to achieve some purely technological goal, such as the maximization of human domination over nature, then its growth is autonomous as well as sustained and irreversible. Such being the case, R&D institutions are not subordinated to or at the service of any other institutions. But, though autonomous, R&D growth, according to this model, is still generated and driven by human decisions, in this case by human decisions to pursue science and technology as ends in themselves. Though autonomous, it is still dependent on rational or free human choice.

It is reasonable to claim that R&D growth is not only sustained, irreversible, and autonomous, but that it is also independent of human rational choice if it can be shown that the human acts which are the driving force behind R&D growth are compulsive. There are two types of cases of compulsive action. A person may be said to have performed some action compulsively if the action was not based, and could not in the circumstances have been based, on any previous choice or deliberation on the person's part. The behavior of the drunkard, the kleptomaniac, the sleepwalker, and the person under hypnosis is compulsive in this sense. Though it may be quite tempting, it seems definitely wrong to suggest that the major supporters and agents of R&D growth are behaving like sleepwalkers, drunkards, kleptomaniacs, or hypnotized subjects. However one may want to characterize their actions, one must surely admit that they are based on choices and that these choices in turn are the consequence of elaborate plans and the careful study of options. But an action which results from choice and deliberation may still be compulsive if the person who performed it could not have been swayed from that decision by any kind of argument or even by any kind of threat or anticipated consequences. Such would be the case perhaps of the man who systematically and with careful deliberation and planning goes about killing every woman he loves; he is undeterred from these actions, no matter how persuasive is the plea of his loved ones or how great the danger of being apprehended or how intense the anticipated remorse after the killing is done. He can thus be deemed compulsive even though he is attentive and careful in the making of his decisions.

If our pursuit of R&D growth is compulsive in this second sense, then the pace and direction of technological growth is not only autonomous but also independent of rational or free human choice. If indeed no set of reasons or no anticipations of impending disaster could possibly move us from our commitment to maximize R&D growth, then it no longer makes sense to say that we have any control over the development of technology. This thesis when conjoined with the previously articulated thesis that technological change is the primary cause of social change would warrant the conclusion that technology is now the master and man the slave, as long of course as technology is not construed in anthropomorphic terms.

But how can technological fetishists establish that our decisions to give top priority to technological development are compulsive? Jacques Ellul suggests at times that the compulsiveness of these decisions is due to the fact that our minds have been completely "technicized." According to him, we operate completely within a framework of technological values, and thus cannot step out of the system in order to criticize these values. Since the goals implicit in the principles of technological rationability (such as, control over nature, efficiency, and R&D growth) are our primary and overarching goals, we cannot weigh their value by reference to other goals; rather, we assess all other goals in terms of their conformity to technological goals. All aspects of civilization, he says, are brought under and are subject to the dictates of the principles of technological rationality.

> Herein lives the inversion we are witnessing. Without exception in the course of history, technique belonged to civilization and was merely a single element in a host of nontechnical activities. Today technique has taken over the whole of civilization. . . . Henceforth every component of civilization is subject to the law that technique is itself civilization. Civilization no longer exists of itself. Every activity—intellectual, artistic, moral—is only part of technique.[6]

In contemporary civilization, we are all inside the technical circle. And, "inside the technical circle, the choice among methods, mechanism, organization, and formulas is carried out automatically."[7]

All this points to the following conclusion: it is impossible to be moved by reasons from our commitment to technological goals, since it is this commitment which today provides the basis for all our practical reasoning. Therefore, our commitment to maximal R&D growth, as well as to other technological goals, is compulsive. But if technological growth is driven by compulsive choices, then it is not driven by free rational choice; therefore, technology is growing independently of free rational choice. So goes one fetishist argument.

But this argument simply won't work. Humans have always had primary and overarching goals. Would this argument have us believe that all people, and not merely the populations of modern technological societies, have always been compulsively attached to their primary and overarching goals? Take someone who follows the love ethic and whose one purpose in life is to spread love, care, and cooperation among all peoples. Are we to say that this commitment, because it is "ultimate," is thereby irrational or unfree? Clearly something has gone wrong here.

Rational persons should be able, at least indirectly, to assess critically their set of primary and overarching goals, though obviously not by reference to other "superior" goals. Surely if their ultimate goals are in conflict, or if the pursuit of them is self-defeating, then they have a prima facie case for seriously modifying them. Suppose that getting people to love, care for, and cooperate with one another resulted in universal boredom and economic misery. This would be prima facie evidence for the conclusion that the love ethic is ultimately self-defeating, since surely part of the point of getting people to love one another is to get them to do good for one another. It would then appear rational for proponents of the love ethic to seriously modify, or abandon totally, their ultimate commitment to get all people to care for and to cooperate with one another. If they could not be moved by this kind of evidence, then this would be good grounds for saying that their commitment to the love ethic is compulsive.

Consequently, even if the goals implicit in technological rationality were our primary and overarching goals, it would not follow that we were compulsively committed to these goals unless it could be shown that we would continue unflinchingly to pursue these goals when it proved self-defeating to do so. It would certainly be self-defeating to pursue as final ends the goals of technology if this led to widespread chaos and destruction, and possibly annihilation, since these consequences would offset any gains made in human mastery over nature through technology. If technological fetishists could show that we would opt for maximum R&D growth even in the face of growing chaos and destruction, then they would have a strong case for saying that our commitment to R&D growth is compulsive, and hence that we have simply lost control over technology.

This indeed is precisely what fetishists, and especially Ellul, have been trying to do (although they do not always seem clearly aware of it). For example, some have gone out of their way to pin the blame for the rise of the modern warfare state with its outlandish defense budgets and sophisticated weapons for annihilation or for the exponential growth of ecological disruption on the imperatives of modern technological development. There is no doubt that a snowballing arms race or snowballing pollution and resource depletion considerably lessen the probabilities for increased human power over nature and history, and in fact lower the prospects for human survival. If the arms race and ecological disruption are a necessary outcome or a necessary means for the achievement of technological goals when the latter are primary and overarching, then it seems obvious that the pursuit of maximal technological growth as an ultimate objective is self-defeating. And if these considerations in no way deter us or the planners from the pursuit of maximal technological growth, then a strong case can be made that we or the planners are compulsively supporting and energizing R&D growth, perhaps as a consequence of constant reinforcement by technocratic institutions. It would then be reasonable to conclude that technology is our master rather than our servant.

We now have clear formulation of the meaning of technological fetishism, and we have straightforward tests for determining either its truth or its falsity, either its plausibility or its implausibility. If indeed the imperatives of technology commit us to a spiraling arms race and increasing ecological breakdown, and if we nevertheless pursue technological growth, then this is prima facie evidence that we have made a fetish of technology, that we have lost control of it, and that it now dominates our lives. Can such a case be made? The key question is whether sustained technological growth requires a spiraling arms race and increasing ecological breakdown. To this question I now turn. I shall examine the evidence that technology is primarily responsible for the arms race in the remainder of this chapter, and in the next chapter I shall examine the evidence that technology is primarily responsible for our ecological crisis.

The Warfare State

Many Dystopian writers have claimed that technological growth depends on intermittent warfare and the constant arms expenditures that this requires. Lumping science and technology together, the anonymous author of *Report from Iron Mountain* states the case quite baldly:

> War is the principal motivational force for the development of science at every level, from the abstractly conceptual to the narrowly technological. Modern society places a high value on "pure" science, but it is historically inescapable that all the significant discoveries that have been made about the natural world have been inspired by the real or imaginary military necessities of their epoch. . . . Beginning with the development of iron and steel, and proceeding through the discoveries of the laws of motion and thermodynamics to the age of the atomic particle, the synthetic polymer, and the space capsule, no important scientific advance has not been at least indirectly initiated by an implicit requirement of weaponry.[8]

But it is John Kenneth Galbraith (clearly not a Dystopian) who has given the most persuasive argument for the claim that the spiraling arms race is due primarily to the needs of technology. This should be no surprise. He does not believe that our system is any longer capitalistic, so he couldn't account for mushrooming defense spending by appealing to the profit interests of capitalist armament industries, to the need to defend capitalism against socialist aggression, or to the requirements of American imperialism. Since he believes America is a technocracy, he can only account for the major tendencies of American domestic and foreign policy by appeal to the needs of technology, and this he does.

Specifically, Galbraith maintains that the channeling of the largest part of federal revenues into defense or defense-allied projects (such as the space race) is indispensable for meeting our growing commitments to technological development. It is obvious, he argues, that the health of our economy requires constantly increasing federal expenditures, or otherwise serious recessions and depressions cannot be avoided. It is also obvious that organized R&D is increasingly important to the health of our economy. In 1921, allocations to R&D constituted only 0.2 percent of the United States GNP; now it constitutes about 3 percent. Allocations for R&D have grown much more quickly than the GNP has grown during the past few decades.

It is agreed on all sides that the private sector of the economy is increasingly less capable of functioning as a major source of support for R&D. Whereas in 1921, government only provided 17 percent of all R&D funds, by 1961 it was providing 65 percent of these funds.[9]

From the above, it seems to follow that only the kind of government spending which at the same time underwrites R&D will be adequate to keep the economy healthy. This apparently contradicts the early views of some economists that what matters is not the nature of government expenditures but the absolute amount when the objective is the maximal stimulation of the economy; the building of pyramids, they thought, would do just as well as anything else. It is at this point that Galbraith makes his key move. According to him, any massive reorientation of government financial priorities from defense and defense-related projects to transportation, housing, health, and welfare would lead to disastrous cutbacks in government R&D and hence to a serious economic slowdown. Galbraith maintains that these other forms of government expenditures cannot be used to underwrite R&D at the level that defense expenditures can and at the level that is required for a healthy economy. This position seems supported by the well-known figures to the effect that defense and defense-related projects, though never commanding much more than 50 percent of government revenues, have provided between 80 and 90 percent of governmental subsidies for R&D. Thus, the cold war and the defense-related allocations which it requires seems to have come into being not because of the rivalry between capitalism and communism but because of the demands of technological growth.[10]

This argument, though initially attractive, cannot in the long run stand up to criticism. The relevant facts show that there is something implausible about the claim that R&D can only be underwritten by the government through very large military or military-related budgets.

Most of the new technology is needed by the civilian sector, which is after all still the largest sector of the United States economy. Yet we are told by Galbraith that the government can only effectively support civilian technology through defense or defense-related expenditures. This means that government-induced growth in civilian R&D is brought about mainly as a byproduct of government-induced growth in military R&D. Government-induced growth in civilian R&D is a spinoff from government-induced growth in military R&D. The government thus underwrites civilian technology mainly by allowing it to appropriate and improve upon or modify inventions or discoveries made for military or military-related purposes. Military R&D has, for example, provided the civilian economy with nuclear power, the computer, the transistor, the jet engine, penicillin, operations research, and systems engineering.

But doesn't it seem rather bizarre to create or expand enormously institutions for defense R&D in order mainly to support civilian R&D? Instead of taking the circuitous route of generating growth in civilian technology as a spinoff from growth in military technology, wouldn't it be less wasteful and more orderly to fund directly the forms of civilian technological growth which are most desirable? Surely we would pay less for and exert more control over civilian R&D if it were subject to direct planning rather than being an accidental spinoff of whatever military technology may be in fashion.

In response to this objection, it might be answered that the new kinds of sophisticated technologies must be developed at the military level before being developed at the civilian level. The military use of the technology is more simple and primitive, thus constituting an indispensable first stage in preparation for the more sophisticated civilian uses. For example, nuclear power was applicable on the military level decades before it became fully applicable for civilian purposes. It could be argued that the problem facing the peaceful use of atomic energy could not be solved if the problems facing its military use had not previously been solved. Among others, Jacques Ellul has argued in this manner.[11]

This response is simply inadequate. What may have been true of nuclear technology is true of few other kinds of technology. Though the computer and the transistor were first developed to serve military objectives, they could have easily been developed independently to serve civilian objectives. And there is no way one could argue that the technology appropriate for the production of primary metals, of electrical machines and meters, of scientific instruments, and of health, transportation, food processing, and machine tools has to go through a military phase before it can meet the sophisticated demands of the civilian economy. Indeed, one could maintain that today defense R&D is so specialized and sophisticated that its products have few if any close civilian analogues and purposes.[12]

More importantly, however, all the evidence indicates that the use of defense and space expenditures primarily as a stimulant for technological growth is both extravagantly wasteful and strikingly ineffective. For one thing, only a very small portion of the defense dollar is devoted to R&D (no more than 20 percent), and only a small portion of the defense R&D dollar is devoted to basic or applied research; approximately 15 percent goes to basic research, 20 percent to applied research, and the remainder to development. Expenditures for development, however, do little for scientific and technological growth.[13]

Furthermore, the spinoff from defense R&D has been much more meager and localized than expected. Patent statistics indicate that only a small percentage of the R&D financed by the defense department or related agencies has resulted in innovations with sufficient commercial application to be patented, and of these only a very small percentage were actually put to commercial use. Whatever spinoff for civilian technology which has come from defense R&D has been concentrated in very few industries. For example, nearly 60 percent of all R&D is locked up in aircrafts and electronics, and over 80 percent if chemistry, motor vehicles, and nonelectric machinery industries are added.[14] Most of the other industries are left by the government to fend for themselves. Thus, the textiles, food processing, paper, and primary metals industries receive little or no government-financed R&D. The scientific instruments industry pays for two-thirds and the primary metals industry for 100 percent, of its R&D. As a result, total public and private spending for R&D in sectors not relevant to the military is proportionately very low. Thus only 3.5 percent of all public and private R&D funds are absorbed by the scientific and professional instruments industry and only 1.5 percent by the primary metals industry.[15]

This distortion in the distribution of R&D funds appears to be causing a serious drag in the technological growth of the more neglected sectors of the economy, but especially in the production of machine tools and in steel, shipbuilding, mass transportation, building construction, and health.[16] These and other scattered pieces of information seem to indicate that the proportionately large commitment of government R&D funds to defense or defense-related agencies is seriously undermining civilian technological growth rather than stimulating it. From the point of view of technology and its development, the growth of the modern warfare state is irrational.

In conclusion, technological fetishism cannot be defended on the ground that we compulsively pursue technological growth even in the face of a dangerously spiraling arms race which this growth necessitates. For the facts are that the arms race is injurious rather than helpful to technological growth. The facts of defense spending thus cannot serve as evidence that our pursuit of maximum technological growth is compulsive and irrational, but perhaps the facts of ecology will do so.

Conclusion

In this chapter I have begun an analysis of technological fetishism, which is a Dystopian view of technology. According to that view, technology has become our master and we its slave. Technology is growing on its own, not as a consequence of free human choice, and technology, in its growth, is shaping all the major institutions and practices of society. I spent most of the chapter attempting to reconstruct the technological fetishist view. The main problem was that the proponents of that view have failed to present it in a clear, coherent, and persuasive manner. I rejected a number of standard interpretations as being wholly implausible or confused. The question was: In what sense could it be plausibly claimed by the technological fetishist that technology is growing independently of free, rational (uncompulsive) choice? My answer was as follows: if the pursuit of technological growth is self-defeating, either because it leads to an endlessly spiraling arms race or because it leads ultimately to ecological disaster, but nonetheless technological growth is chosen in the face of all these facts, then the choice to pursue technological growth is compulsive, and hence unfree.

I asked whether a spiraling arms race was necessary for technological growth. I concluded that the evidence pointed the other way. If anything, the shifting of resources toward defense spending hinders, rather than stimulates, balanced technological growth. Generally, the Dystopian claim that technology is primarily at fault for the arms race seems mistaken. Can the other two views, the Utopian and the Socialist, account any better for the American arms economy? For the Utopian, it is an embarrassment. If technology is not supporting the arms economy, it does not seem to be effectively working against it either. Indeed, the needs of technology seem to be subordinated to the arms economy. Socialists recently have attempted to give a detailed account of the growing arms economy since World War II. The functions of the arms economy in America, they say, are to defeat socialism abroad, to provide protection for foreign investment, to stimulate the home economy, and to provide large, ensured profits for the major firms, most of whom receive defense contracts.[17] The Socialist view on the functions of the arms economy seem more plausible than the Dystopian or Utopian views. Nonetheless, there may be alternative accounts which compete with the Socialist account, but which are neither Utopian nor Dystopian.

But if technological growth does not account for the spiraling arms race, perhaps it accounts for the intensifying ecological crisis. If such is the case, then technological fetishism still has a chance of being true. We turn now to the issue of the ecological crisis.

Notes

[1]Philip Slater, *The Pursuit of Loneliness* (Boston: Beacon, 1970), p. 44.

[2]Jacques Ellul, *Technological Society* (New York: Vintage, 1964), p. 133.

[3]Ibid., p. 85.

[4]Ibid., p. 97.

[5]Ibid., pp. 89–90.

[6]Ibid., pp. 128–130.

[7]Ibid., p. 82.

[8]*Report from Iron Mountain on the Possibility and Desirability of Peace* (New York: Dial, 1967), p. 53.

[9]John Kenneth Galbraith, *New Industrial State* (New York: New American Library, 1967), pp. 228–230, 339–346; Richard Nelson, Morton J. Peck, and Edward Kalachek, *Technology, Economic Growth, and Public Policy* (Washington, D.C.: Brookings Institution, 1967), p. 46.

[10]Nathan Rosenberg, *Technology and American Economic Growth* (New York: Harper, 1972), p. 182; H. L. Nieburg, *In the Name of Science* (Chicago: Quadrangle, 1970), p. 78.

[11]Ellul, *Technological Society*, p. 99.

[12]Nelson, et al., *Technology, Economic Growth, and Public Policy*, pp. 82–85; Rosenberg, p. 184.

[13]Richard J. Barnet, *The Economy of Death* (New York: Atheneum, 1970), pp. 48–55; Rosenberg, *Technology and American Economic Growth*, pp. 176–177.

[14]Ibid.

[15]Richard Barber, *The American Corporation* (New York: Dutton, 1970), p. 138; Nelson, et al., *Technology, Economic Growth, and Public Policy*, pp. 49–52, 82–85; Rosenberg, *Technology and American Economic Growth*, p. 182.

[16]Seymour Melman, *Pentagon Capitalism* (New York: McGraw-Hill, 1970), pp. 186–197; Seymour Melman, "The Big Machine Breaks Down," *The Nation*, March 20, 1972, pp. 361–365.

[17]Cf. Michael Reich and David Finkelhor, "The Military-Industrial Complex: No Way Out," in Tom Christoffel, David Finkelhor, and Dan Gilbarg, eds., *Up Against The American Myth* (New York: Holt, Rinehart and Winston, 1970), pp. 73–109.

10

Alienation from Nature

Technology and Ecological Disorder

No doubt much of the new popularity of the Dystopian view is due to
the growing ecological crisis. It is quite easy to blame modern technology for pollution and resource depletion. It is certainly true that
ecological problems have become critical only since the advent of modern technology. It is tempting to believe that the only way out of our
ecological crisis is to dismantle the apparatus of modern industrial and
postindustrial technology. The historical role of modern technology is
supposed to have been to bring us affluence; now it appears that
technology cannot do this and that any attempt to make it do this can
only wreak disaster.

Dystopians claim that technological growth is the primary cause of
our ecological crisis. This view is attractive, but is it ultimately correct?
To find out, we must look at the various explanations for the ecological
crisis here in America.

Moralist and Institutionalist Explanations

Obviously, in order to deal with our environmental crisis we must
determine which factors have contributed most to its irruption and
continued intensification in the face of impending disaster. Most of the

explanations already given are either moralist or institutionalist. A moralist explanation blames our ecological crisis on individual people or masses of people; an institutionalist explanation blames it on institutions. Moralists focus on individual attitudes, motives, or life-styles, whereas institutionalists focus on the goals and needs of institutions. According to moralists, it is mainly people (persons acting in their own individual capacity) who excessively procreate, pollute, and exploit nature. Institutionalists, of course, do not deny that people do these things; what they emphasize is that institutions (such as governments and corporations) are primarily responsible for the ecologically bad behavior of individuals. For moralists, the ecological crisis is ultimately caused by an excessive desire in people to procreate, by their desire to dominate or subjugate nature, and by their greed, wastefulness, and compulsive consumerism. Institutionalists do not deny that these desires and attitudes in individuals are among the causes of excessive population growth, pollution, and resource depletion. However, they insist on two things. First, these desires and attitudes are caused and reinforced as a consequence of the needs and goals of major institutions. For example, wastefulness and compulsive consumerism are instilled in people by capitalist institutions whose health depends on planned obsolescence and continually increasing spending. Second, though people may have ecologically sound attitudes (such as frugality and philanthropy) they are not allowed by our institutions to counterbalance effectively the ecologically unsound attitudes. For example, a corporate employee may have a strong desire not only to maximize profits but also to contribute to clean air and water. But as long as the employee is acting for the corporation clean air and water must be subordinated to profit. Within the framework of the corporation profit is always an *effective* motive, whereas the desire to clean up air and water often is not.

Among ecological critics Paul Ehrlich and Lynn White have tended to give moralist explanations for the ecological crisis in America; Barry Commoner, Garret Harding, Kenneth Boulding, Ralph Nader, and Jacques Ellul have tended to give institutionalist explanations. Moralists have been slightly more successful in explaining the population crisis, and institutionalists, the pollution and resource crises. Thus, moralists have tended to try to reduce all ecological problems ultimately to the population problem ("too many people" accounts for pollution and resource depletion), whereas institutionalists have tended to play down the importance of the population problem.

Dystopians and Socialists both tend to give an institutionalist account of the ecological crisis in America; they specifically focus on the federal government and major corporations. But they view these institutions quite differently. Socialists believe corporations to be controlled by capitalists and to be oriented primarily toward the maximization of profits; the government is, according to them, controlled by the corporations. Dystopians do not have such a coherent and united view, but, at the very least, they believe corporations and government to be becoming increasingly technocratic (that is, increasingly subject to the dictates of technicians and the goals implicit in technological rationality). And whatever else they may attribute to the government and corporations, they conceive of these institutions as irretrievably committed to technological growth, no matter what the consequences. Socialists thus blame the ecological crisis in America on the capitalist goals of American corporations and government, whereas Dystopians blame it on their technocratic goals; the former, on institutionalized profit maximization, and the latter on institutionalized technological growth and expansion of human power over nature.

It is not easy to tell who are closer to the truth, moralists or institutionalists; and, among institutionalists, Dystopians (blaming institutionalized technology) or Socialists (blaming institutionalized capitalism). In this chapter I shall attempt to give a provisional assessment. However, it must be kept in mind that there are three basic kinds of ecological crises: population, pollution, and resource depletion. What counts as a good explanation for one of these may not for the others, so I shall examine each of these topics singly, starting with population.

Population

In 1650, the world population was growing at a rate of 0.3 percent per year, with a doubling time of 250 years; by 1970, it was growing at a rate of 2.1 percent per year, with a doubling time of 33 years.[1] The dominant historical fact during the period extending from 1650 to 1970 is of course the emergence and flowering of industrial technology. This correlation between the dramatic rise in the rates of population growth and the world-wide spread of industrial societies can easily tempt one to take an institutionalist stance and to blame the population crisis on the needs or imperatives of industrial institutions. However, the most obvious and least controversial facts about modern population growth initially seem more supportive of the moralist position. Population growth is a function of two countervailing factors, the birth rate and the death rate. If the birth rate increases and/or the death rate decreases, then the rate of population growth will increase. Industrialization, through advancements in agricultural and health technologies, has led to a dramatic decrease in the death rate. Meanwhile, there has been only a relatively small and belated compensatory decrease in the birth rate. Why has not the birth rate declined as quickly as the death rate?

Moralists answer that the birth rate has not declined as quickly as the death rate because people want to procreate; they have always wanted to do so, and will continue to want to do so unless prevented or otherwise discouraged. That the birth rate should have resisted any decline simultaneous with and proportional to the decline of the death rate, during and after the onset of industrialization, is for moralists firm evidence of the relative dependence of the population crisis on personal motives and life-styles and of its relative independence of industrial institutions.

To this institutionalists could answer that, even if the average birth rates changed only minimally during and after the onset of industrialization, it does not follow that industrialization had little or no direct impact on the birth rate. It might have been in the interest of industrial institutions to maintain the birth rates at an artificially high level rather than to allow them to immediately and proportionately follow the declining death rates. How else, according to institutionalists, could we account for the tendency of industrial peoples to populate at a greater rate than preindustrial peoples in the face of the fact that the bearing of children is economically more costly and less rewarding for industrial peoples than it was for preindustrial peoples?[2] Perhaps this is because the bearing of children has a symbolic value for industrial peoples which reflects the needs of the industrial system.

There is a straightforward way for provisionally testing the competing claims of the moralist and institutionalist theories of modern population growth. If the high rates of population growth typical of modern societies are a hindrance to industrial development, then the moralist theory is supported; if they are important contributory factors or necessary conditions for industrial development, then the institutionalist theory is supported. Industrial development is inextricably tied to sustained economic growth, so whether or not the moralist or institutionalist theory is most correct depends on whether high rates of population growth are an aid or an obstacle to sustained economic growth. On this point, there are two models of economic growth: the *Malthusian model* (named after the nineteenth-century economist Thomas Malthus) seems to support the moralist view; the *Keynesian model* (named after the twentieth-century economist John Maynard Keynes) seems to support the institutionalist view.

According to the Malthusian model, supply rather than demand, or production rather than consumption, constitutes the major obstacle to economic growth; there is constant danger that the forces of production will prove inadequate to avoid economic stagnation or regression. This view is based on the assumptions of a relatively fixed supply of land and nonrenewable resources and of a relative scarcity of savings available for capital investment. In the light of these assumptions, it can be argued that population growth tends to depress per capita production. As population rises, the supply of land, and nonrenewable resources per capita decreases, thus bringing into play the "law of diminishing returns." Furthermore, with a high rate of population growth income tends to be diverted excessively from savings to consumption, thus depleting the pool of investment funds. Even the investment funds which are available tend excessively to be put to relatively unproductive uses (such as housing) rather than to more productive uses (such as heavy machinery). According to the Malthusian model, population growth is therefore a hindrance rather than an aid to industrial development. This model thus undermines the institutionalist view that the needs of industrial institutions have been the primary cause of the rapid growth of population in the modern world.

The Malthusian model, however, suffers from one glaring weakness: it fails to consider the dramatic role of technology in consistently expanding (or providing substitutes for) the supposedly fixed stock of nonrenewable resources, and in consistently increasing the productivity of land and capital. Increased productivity means increased income per worker, and increased income per worker entails a rising propensity to save, and with it, a growing pool of funds available for investment. Technology then tends to attenuate, if not eliminate, the scarcity of resources and investment funds. This explains why growth in production in industrial societies has easily outpaced growth in population, and hence why per capita production has been able to increase significantly in the face of expanding population.

The Keynesian model, on the other hand, makes generous allowances for the influence of technology on production. According to it, the obstacles to economic growth come not from supply (or from productive capacity) but from demand (or from consumption). That is, the drag on economic growth comes mainly from the tendency of consumption to lag behind productive capacity or, equivalently, from the tendency of proposed investments to lag behind savings. If people save too much, or do not consume all that is produced, then the producers will cut back on production, laying off workers and driving down total income; this further depresses consumption, setting off in turn more cutbacks in production, and more unemployment. For Keynesians, the major problem is not getting producers to produce more, but getting consumers to consume more.

Within the framework of the Keynesian model population growth may appear as a welcome stimulant for economic growth, not only because it diverts funds from savings to consumption, but also because it creates additional demand for the sorts of goods (such as housing and utilities) which require a large flow of investment capital.

Hence, according to the Keynesian model, population growth aids rather than hinders industrial development; this model then supports the institutionalist rather than the moralist account of the population crisis. Not all Keynesians, however, would say that population growth is indispensable for industrial development (though some, such as Alvin Hansen, have).[3]

Which model is correct to describe industrial societies, the Malthusian or the Keynesian? Some economists have suggested that each applies to a particular stage of industrial development, the Malthusian model to societies which are newly industrialized or on the verge of industrialization (when technology is indeed crude and savings are scarce), and the Keynesian model to advanced, mass consumption, industrial societies (when technology is sophisticated and savings are overabundant).[4]

It should be noted, however, that the Malthusian model does not fully support the moralist view (the view in this case that population growth is not due primarily to the needs of industrial institutions). For there remains a number of reasons why population growth, within limits, would contribute to the economic development even of undeveloped industrial societies. Population growth allows for the institution of economies of scale; it tends to result in a population skewed toward youth rather than old age (and thus more amenable to rapid change); it is an "inducement mechanism" for economic growth, insofar as it imposes pressure for a more effective use of resources, capital stock, labor and technology; it provides more potential contributors to the existing stock of knowledge; and, finally, it provides more security for venturesome entrepreneurial undertakings.[5]

There is no question, however, that if population continues to grow at the present pace the results will be disastrous. This is not the issue here. The issue is what has caused the striking increases in the rate of population growth in the modern world. Has the primary cause been the needs of the industrial system, as the institutionalists contend, or the (perhaps inexplicable) universal drive that people have to procreate, as the moralists contend? The institutionalists' case is quite strong, I think, but not fully convincing. One would have to concede, given the meagerness of the evidence, that it is difficult to decide which side is right. (It goes without saying that it is more difficult to decide who is closer to the truth, the institutionalists who ultimately blame technology—such as the Dystopians—or the institutionalists who ultimately blame profits—the Socialists—in their account of the population crisis.) Perhaps we will get more definitive answers about the relative adequacy of the institutionalist and moralist views when we discuss the causes of the pollution and nonrenewable resource crises. But first we have to determine whether the pollution and resource crises are simply the result of the population crisis.

Population and the Ecological Crisis

Is our crisis in pollution and resource conservation caused mainly by the population crisis, as many seem to suggest? If population growth were to stop, would growth in pollution and resource depletion also stop? Moralists sometimes seem to argue this way.[6] We have too much pollution and too little resources, they say, primarily because we have too many people. They say we should put all our energies into solving the population problem.

This position, however, seems unjustifiable. Though population growth is surely a contributory factor in pollution and nonrenewable resource depletion, it does not seem to be the only or primary cause. The extent to which a given community successfully maintains itself in ecological equilibrium depends more on the nature and quality of a population than on its number. Even the moralist Paul Ehrlich (of *The Population Bomb*) concedes this in a letter answering his critics:

> The most serious population growth occurs among the affluent whites of the U. S. A., and their analogues in Western Europe, the Soviet Union, and the Japanese. These people are the prime looters and polluters of our planet—the ones who are destroying our life support systems. From the point of view of pollution, every American child born is 50 times the disaster for the world as each Indian child. From the point of view of consumption, each American is 300 times as bad as each Indonesian.[7]

Claims that population growth is the primary cause of general ecological disruption can be countered by the following two arguments. First, advanced Western nations (plus Japan) generate more pollution than any other comparable group and cause more resource depletion than the other nations combined. Yet their population constitutes only a small proportion of the world population, and their rate of population growth is among the lowest in the world. Second, the rate of growth of pollution and depletion of nonrenewable resources, in advanced Western nations (plus Japan) especially, and in the rest of the world generally, is greatly outpacing the rate of population growth in these same countries.

Pollution

Many have been inclined to blame people rather than institutions for the enormous increases in air and water pollution in America since World War II. A typical moralist view is the following:

> For the villain of the piece is not some profit-hungry industrialist, nor some lax public official who can be replaced. The villains are consumers,

who demand (or at least let themselves be cajoled into demanding) new, more, faster, bigger, cheaper playthings without counting the cost of a dirtier, smellier, sicklier world.[8]

The moralist claim that the people (consumers) are ultimately to blame for pollution is based on the assumption of consumer sovereignty, the assumption that ultimately consumers determine what is to be produced and how it is to be produced. However, it seems to me that the thesis of consumer sovereignty, and hence the moralist view, is somewhat implausible in contemporary America, as the following remarks will suggest.

Consumer sovereignty can exist only where the following two conditions are met. First, corporations must exert little or no control over consumer wants and values. Second, within the limits of available resources, the corporate system (in conjunction with the government) must provide satisfaction for all important consumer wants; there is no important demand for which there is not an appropriate supply. If consumers demand mini-skirts and wide ties, and resources are available, corporations will supply mini-skirts and wide ties. Obviously, consumers would not be sovereign if under these circumstances they were supplied only with midi-dresses and narrow ties.

As is well known, these two conditions will tend to be met in a perfectly competitive market system where no corporation has discretionary control over prices, and will tend not to be met in monopoly or oligopoly market systems where corporations authoritatively determine prices. In a perfectly competitive market system, corporations do not have the resources for the elaborate advertising campaigns required for control over consumer tastes and they cannot pass the added costs on to consumers. And the second condition cannot be flouted without sustained collusion, by definition absent from the perfectly competitive market system. On the other hand, collusion and a heavy commitment to advertising (with costs passed on to consumers) are the normal pattern for oligopoly and monopoly firms. The consumer can be deemed sovereign in perfectly competitive markets, and the corporation sovereign in monopoly or oligopoly markets. The consumer can be assigned responsibility for the pollution generated through the use or production of goods in the competitive market, and the corporation for the pollution generated in the oligopoly or monopoly markets.

It seems that most of the air pollution in the United States is due to the transactions of monopoly or oligopoly firms. That is, air pollution is due mainly to the goods produced by, or the methods of production of, the automobile, utilities, oil, coal, chemicals, and primary metals industries, all of which are highly concentrated or on the verge of becoming highly concentrated. It has been argued, for example, that as much as 60 percent of all air pollution in the United States comes from the automobile.[9] (In the case of water pollution, it is more difficult to determine the respective roles of the perfectly competitive and of the oligopoly-monopoly markets.)

Consumers, for example, do not appear to have been sovereign in the area of transportation. Automobile producers have used their oligopolistic power strenuously and, more often than not, effectively. Automobile producers have poured in large sums of money to control consumer preferences (such as for the automobile as opposed to other means of transportation, for large as opposed to small automobiles, for tail fins and other bizarre designs). Only recently, mainly because of the energy crisis and the recession, have the major automobile manufacturers begun to run into serious resistance to their attempts at manipulation.

Furthermore, it can hardly be denied that the vehicle and transportation industries have failed to satisfy many consumer wants, whatever their origin. Seemingly, consumers want safer and longer-lasting cars, more mass transportation, and cleaner air. Can it be argued that consumers are nonetheless to blame because they do not want these things badly enough to pay the extra costs? I do not think so. It has been shown that the overall costs of a longer-lasting, safer, and ecologically cleaner car might well be less than today's gas guzzler. For example, a car without the ecologically inefficient internal combustion engine (such as, perhaps, a steam or electric car) would most probably be simpler and less costly. If style changes were made less frequently, or were eliminated, the price of cars would be reduced dramatically.[10] It is also well known that the automobile industry, not consumers, has constantly opposed the introduction of federal standards regarding pollution emission from cars.[11]

Why haven't consumers increased demands for public transportation? Clearly consumers are opting for whatever public services there are of this sort. But often services are cut back even as the number of patrons increases. Is it because consumers are not willing to pay enough for these public transportation services? Again, the most ardent opponents of public transportation, and the most ardent supporters of federally financed highway construction, are the automobile producers, not the consumers. The massive building of highways, in turn, has led to the exodus of homeowners, shopping centers, and factories from the central city, and from the points of convergence of traditional transportation routes. In the private sector, there is good evidence that the outside financier controllers of private passenger railroads had more to do with their demise or ill-health then consumers. These interests, for example, have tended to use railroad profits to finance outside ventures rather than to modernize railway services.[12]

It seems reasonable to conclude that corporations have greater sovereignty than consumers in the areas of production and consumption most relevant to air pollution, and hence that corporations are more to blame than consumers for the air pollution emanating from the production or the consumption of goods. On the issue of air pollution, the institutionalist account of our ecological crisis seems preferable to the moralist account. But what sort of institutionalist account fits the facts best—the Socialist account which blames pollution in America on the profit-maximizing needs of capitalist corporations, or the Dystopian account which blames it on the imperatives of technology within a presumably technocratic corporate system? The issue therefore is whether the tendency of corporations to pollute excessively is due to the needs of capitalism or to the needs of technology.

Pollution: The Capitalist and Technological Causes

Barry Commoner, in his stimulating and popular *The Closing Circle*, argues that both the needs of capitalism and the imperatives of technology account for the growth of the polluting activities of American corporations.[13] However, his arguments pointing to the needs of capitalism are more persuasive than those pointing to the imperatives of technology. According to Commoner, pollution has increased dramatically since World War II because it has become more profitable to produce goods or to use production methods which pollute more.

Since World War II, goods which tended to pollute less have been replaced by goods which tend to pollute more; for example,

> natural fibers (cotton and wool) have been replaced by synthetic ones; steel and lumber have been displaced by aluminum, plastics, and concrete; railroad freight has been replaced by truck freight; returnable bottles have been displaced by non-returnable ones. On the road, the low-powered automobile engines of the 1920's and 1930's have been replaced by high-powered ones.[14]

The same is true for means of production:

> On the farm, while per capita production has remained about constant, the amount of harvested acreage has decreased; in effect, fertilizer has displaced land. Older methods of insect control have been displaced by synthetic pesticides, such as DDT, and for controlling weeds the cultivator has been displaced by the herbicide spray. Range-feeding of livestock has been displaced by feedlots.[15]

Commoner points out that a significantly higher rate of profit accrues to the new kinds of goods (such as detergents, synthetic clothing, aluminum, and plastics) than to the old kinds of goods these have replaced (such as soap, cotton clothing, steel, and lumber); the same is true for the newer methods of production.[16] So profits are much to blame for the pollution caused by institutional corporate activity since World War II.

How about technology and its imperatives? Here Commoner's case is less clear. Technology is of relevance to pollution either because of the perspectives it brings to bear on major decision-making or the values it imposes.

Let us look at the issue of perspectives first. According to Commoner, there is a sort of tunnel vision implicit in technology which makes it unable to consider all relevant factors when it is applied to the resolution of any problem. Consider his favorite example. The dumping of organic refuse in natural bodies of water destroys their life-support system, for the conversion of these organic wastes into inorganic residues tends to deplete the supply of oxygen needed by other organisms. Enter the technician, whose solution is to transform the organic wastes into inorganic residues in the sewage control plant, and to dump the harmless inorganic residues in rivers and lakes. Unfortunately, these residues are ideal nutrients for algae which bloom furiously and whose decay requires the large amounts of oxygen previously depleted by organic wastes.

> The reason for this failure is clear: the technologist defined his problem too narrowly, taking into his field of vision only one segment of what in nature is an endless cycle that will collapse if stressed anywhere.[17]

But why should this tendency to define a problem too narrowly be implicit in technological thinking? Here Commoner relies for his answer mainly on Galbraith's famous description of the imperatives of technology in *The New Industrial State.*

> Technology means the systematic application of scientific or other organized knowledge to practical tasks. Its most important consequence, at least for the purpose of economics, is in forcing the division and subdivision of any such task into its component parts. Thus, and only thus, can organized knowledge be brought to bear on performance.[18]

That is, the narrowness of technology comes from its tendency to microfractionalize maximally the expertise and the tasks involved in production; the narrowness of technical efficiency is based on its commitment to maximal division of labor.

But here Commoner seems confused. From the fact that technology requires that tasks be microfractionalized, it does not follow that it requires that they be made autonomous or unaccountable to more general needs or imperatives. Indeed, the division of labor has necessarily entailed the integration of tasks and the socialization of production. Furthermore, Commoner seems to ignore the fact that major improvements in the technology of planning, management, and systems have been an essential ingredient in the postindustrial revolution in technology.

The perspective that technology brings to bear on any problem is thus not necessarily tunnel-visioned as Commoner seems to claim; in virtue of its perspective technology is not necessarily a cause of pollution. What of the values that technology brings to bear on major decisions; doesn't the technologist stress productivity above everything else, and isn't increasing productivity a major cause of pollution? After all, hasn't Commoner shown that much of the postwar increases in pollution are due to the introduction of new techniques of production?

Here again we must be careful. We must keep in mind that productivity is a relative concept. A technology which is found to be more productive according to one system of accounts may be deemed less productive according to another. Productivity is measured by the ratio of gains over costs or, equivalently, the ratio of the value of the output over the costs of the inputs. For the capitalist firm, gains are measured by reference to the revenue of the firm, and costs by reference to the payments which the firm has to make. Pollution is not normally a cost for the capitalist firm (unless it is forced upon it as a cost). So it is not unusual that increases in capitalist productivity are accompanied by increases in pollution.

But productivity could also be measured from a social point of view; here we would have a system of social, rather than private, accounts. In a system of social accounts, all losses of good things (such as, clean air) would count as costs and only the output of useful goods would count as gains. So understood, social productivity could well decrease while capitalist productivity increases. And everything else being equal, social productivity will decrease as long as pollution increases.

If corporations were technocratic (as Dystopians seem to believe), would they use some system of private accounts (in which pollution is not included in the calculation of costs) or a system of social accounts (in which pollution is included)? It is difficult to tell. But it does seem that institutions primarily committed to the principles of technological rationality would opt for some system of social accounts. Technocratic institutions are committed to the goal of expanding human control over the social and natural environments. Any addition to the amount of environmental control is a gain; any loss of such control is a cost. A steam engine does work for us (for instance, it may drive a locomotive) and thus adds to our power over our environment; that is the technocratic gain. But it transforms useful energy (present in coal, for example) into unusable energy (heat); that is the technocratic cost. From the point of view of a technocratic system, productivity is in part the ratio of gains in human environmental control over losses in environmental control. If such is the case, then pollution, being a form of noncontrol or loss in control, is clearly a cost for technocratic systems. No human planned or explicitly decided to bring about the enormous increases in pollution since World War II. This pollution growth indeed has been the unintended and undesired byproduct of a whole number of individual decisions having to do with other matters. However, anything which grows in an unplanned or undesired way grows in an uncontrolled way. Furthermore, whether planned or unplanned, pollution growth increasingly imposes severe restrictions on health and recreation and on the sensory appearance of the environment, and thus it severely limits our life options. This again implies diminished individual and collective control over our social and natural environments. It follows that any technological innovation which cuts back on pollution while leaving everything else the same increases the productivity of technocratic systems since it reduces the unit input costs per unit output gained. But it introduces no change in the productivity of capitalist institutions since the reduction of pollution costs is of no relevance to private profit-maximization cost analysis.

The institutionalist account of the pollution crisis seems more plausible than the moralist account. The question is, in virtue of what goal are the major American institutions contributing to the pollution crisis? Is it in virtue of their alleged capitalist goals (such as profit maximization), or their alleged technocratic goals (such as control over nature)? Socialists would prefer the former explanation, Dystopians the latter. But capitalist goals seem to account better for the present pollution crisis than technocratic goals. Socialists then seem to be closer to the truth than Dystopians on the issue of the causes of pollution. Capitalism, rather than technology, seems primarily to blame.

Nonrenewable Resources

There is little question now, given present trends, that key nonrenewable mineral resources (such as lead, mercury, manganese, tin, and tungsten) will be severely depleted in the not-too-distant future.[19] The only issue is how long it will take before the real crisis hits. The problem is simply that the extraction of nonrenewable mineral resources, already very large, is growing every year at a rate approaching 4 percent.[20] It is obvious that this cannot last forever, and that the rate of growth of mineral extraction has to be stopped at some time or other, preferably sooner than later.

There are some who thought that growth of mineral extraction could go on indefinitely. They looked forward to the successive exploitation of lower grade ores, exploration into outer space, and increased recycling. But even if these options opened up indefinite opportunities, they would still raise further insurmountable ecological difficulties. Each would require continued increases in the input of energy for every output of mineral resource. Obviously, the lower grade an ore is or the farther away it is in outer space, the more energy one has to expend for each unit extracted. Similarly, the more one resorts to recycling minerals from increasingly dissipated waste of increasingly complex composition and impurity, the more energy input is required per unit of output. But most energy resources available to us now are nonrenewable and are being depleted at an alarming rate. Will the introduction of renewable energy resources like solar energy save the day? Apparently not. The technical obstacles to full conversion to solar energy are mind boggling. But even if these are overcome, further ecological constraints will appear. For one thing, the use of increasingly more energy inevitably leads to the emission of more pollution, at least in the form of thermal pollution (i.e., waste heat). Now, it may well be the case that thermal efficiency will continue to improve, but this would only be a short-term solution. As long as the use of energy keeps increasing exponentially, the absolute amount of thermal pollution will ultimately increase beyond tolerable bounds even after the maximally feasible efficiency is reached (which of course can never be 100 percent). Clearly, then, there is no way to avoid the conclusion that growth in extraction of minerals must come to an end sometime, and most probably within the next century.

Resource Depletion and Economic Growth

Resource depletion is an international problem, but advanced nations, especially the United States, bear disproportionately the greatest burden of responsibility. It has often been repeated that the United States, with 6 percent of the world's population, consumes between 30 percent and 50 percent of the world's mineral resources, and 35 percent of its energy resources. And the demand by the United States for nonrenewable resources continues to go up at an exponential rate.[21]

But why does the United States extract or demand an increased amount of resources each year? The obvious answer seems to be that the United States is committed to or cannot otherwise do without continued annual economic growth. It is this drive toward continued economic growth which accounts in part for the annual growth in resource extraction.

But what makes the American economy tend to grow? Socialists would point to the needs of corporate capitalism, and Dystopians to the imperatives of technology. Which of these answers is the most plausible? Let us look at the Dystopian answer first.

Technology and Economic Growth

Consider the following argument which might be preferred by a Dystopian (though as far as I know no one has put it in quite this form). Technocratic institutions are irretrievably committed to growth in human power over nature. Growth in human power over nature presupposes technological growth. Technological growth presupposes economic growth, that is, growth in the gross national product (GNP). Therefore, technocratic institutions are irretrievably committed to growth in the GNP. Thus, it is the technocratic nature of the present corporate system which explains its compulsive commitment to growth in the GNP.

This argument, I think, goes wrong on many points. I do not see any necessary connection between growth in human power over nature or growth in technology and growth in GNP; that is, there is no necessary connection between growth in human power over nature or growth in technology and growth in individual consumption, corporate investment, and government spending. Indeed, growth in GNP may actually inhibit growth in human power over nature. Growth in GNP may entail continued increases in pollution and resource depletion, and pollution and resource depletion clearly reduce our collective power over nature.

Conversely, there are a number of ways in which a society can increase the collective power of its members through technological growth without resorting to increases in the GNP (in individual consumption, corporate investment, and government spending). By raising productivity while keeping production constant, a society increases the leisure available to its members; but increased leisure means increased power to dispose of one's time as one wills. A society can improve upon its goods and services (say, by producing tires that last longer or a transportation system which is more reliable). It can decrease its "external diseconomies" by cleaning up its air and rivers, reducing congestion, stress, and crime, and by more effectively conserving its resources. While keeping the per capita intake of goods and services constant, a society can increase the variety of these goods and services as well as employment opportunities and life-styles. By encouraging sustained scientific and technological growth, a society can increase its ability to anticipate and thereby control future events. Power, of course, is a function not only of available minerals and energy, but also of available organized information. Computers, for example, are greatly expanding human power over the environment though requiring only small mineral and energy inputs.

In conclusion, it seems that growth in technologically induced power over nature is perfectly compatible with no growth in the GNP. Indeed, it appears that the imperatives of economic growth, insofar as they entail ecological disaster, will become increasingly incompatible with increased human power over nature and hence with the imperatives of technological rationality. Thus the international resource crisis, when it does occur, can hardly be blamed on technocratic institutions, or on the imperatives of technology, or on technological growth. The Dystopian position here seems unjustified.

Capitalism and Economic Growth

Can the apparently compulsive drive in America toward continued economic growth (growth in the GNP) be blamed on the needs of capitalism as Socialists contend? Here I think a plausible case can be made. It can be argued that capitalism needs economic growth for its political and economic health. The argument would go as follows.

Economic growth takes the form both of growth in wealth (such as the stocks of productive machinery, durable goods, and savings) and growth in income (such as in the production of machinery and of durable and nondurable goods, in services, and in the flow of new purchasing power). Let us see what would happen to a capitalist economy if each of these kinds of growth were stopped.

ELIMINATION OF GROWTH IN TOTAL INCOME

Assume that total income is not allowed to grow beyond a certain level, though wealth is allowed to grow (because people save on their constant incomes). What would be the impact? Consider first the case of the rich investors. If their wealth continues to grow as their incomes remain constant, then the rate of return on investment will continue to get smaller. As the rate of return gets smaller, the rich will be less inclined to invest their wealth productively and production will tend to contract rather than remain constant, thus leading to recession and depression. Of course, the incomes of the investors could be allowed to rise at the expense of the incomes of noninvesting workers, but that would only exacerbate the already increasing class antagonisms.

Consider now the case of the poor. As long as income is not redistributed, they no longer have any hope of improving their economic fate. In the past, their incomes grew along with those of the rich, so it was easier for the poor to tolerate inequality of income. Once total income is frozen, however, the poor can no longer be expected to accept their lowly position as passively as before. The poor would resist and class antagonisms would increase. But if transfer of income was made from rich to poor, thus neutralizing class conflict by appeasing the poor and the deprived, the dangers of recession and depression would be increased. Now the rate of return on total wealth would be even lower, further dampening the tendency to invest.

ELIMINATION OF GROWTH IN WEALTH

Ultimately, growth in wealth must be eliminated also. As long as our stock of assets grows (in the form of machinery and durable and non-durable goods), the stock of extracted natural resources must grow also. But the stock of extracted natural resources, as was argued above, cannot grow endlessly. Ultimately, all natural resources must be recycled, thus creating a constant stock of resources and wealth.

No-growth in wealth would undermine the foundations of capitalism, again for economic and political reasons. First, in a stationary-wealth society total income would have to be small enough to allow sufficient savings only to finance the replacement of worn-out machinery and used-up goods. Initially this would entail a fall in real income, for, in the periods immediately preceding the freeze on growth in wealth, there would be enough income to finance new machines and products as well as to replace worn-out machinery and used-up products. But who would bear the brunt of this curtailment of total income, the rich or the poor? Everything else being equal, the rich would have to bear it. For the rich, not the poor, are the "savers." The rich can resist this by increasing their consumption, thus curtailing their savings but not their total income. Then the others, mainly non-savers, would have to consume less. This again could only exacerbate the struggle between the rich and the poor.

Though the rate of return on investment would now be constant, the rich would have no incentive to invest merely to replace machinery, since their wealth could not grow. (The whole point of investment by a capital owner is to increase his wealth.) A tendency not to invest would lead to recession and depression.

It seems that if capitalism were to eliminate economic growth, it would face serious, and perhaps insurmountable, political and economic difficulties. Thus it appears that capitalism needs constant economic growth for its political and economic health. We can conclude that the tendency of the American economy to grow is best explained by reference to the needs of capitalism rather than to the imperatives of technology. This means that the resource depletion crisis in America can best be explained by reference to the needs of capitalism.

Conclusion

In this chapter I have analyzed the Dystopian claim that technology is primarily to blame for our present ecological crisis. To test this claim, I have had to distinguish between different kinds of explanations for our ecological crisis: moralist explanations (which ultimately lay the blame on groups or individual persons) and institutionalist explanations (which ultimately lay the blame on institutions, especially on the corporate system). Then I distinguished between Dystopian institutionalist explanations (which focus on the role of the imperatives of technology within the corporate system) and Socialist institutionalist explanations (which focus on the role of capitalist goals within the corporate system). On the issue of population growth, I found that a strong case could be made for both the moralist and the institutionalist explanations. On the issues of pollution and resource depletion, it seemed to me that the institutionalist explanations were unquestionably more plausible than the moralist explanations. Among institutionalist explanations, I found the Socialist explanations (that the needs of capitalism are ultimately to blame for the pollution and resource depletion crises) to be superior to the Dystopian explanations (that the imperatives of technology are ultimately to blame for the pollution and resource depletion crises).

Epilog to Part Two

We are now ready to discuss the Socialist view of the relation of technology to society. We have encountered it a number of times in our discussion of the Dystopian view. Both the Dystopians and the Socialists agree that the use of technology in the United States has had and continues to have many bad effects, and indeed that, on balance, technology in the United States is generating more regress than progress, more ill than good. Dystopians and Socialists, however, disagree in their explanations, the Dystopians ultimately putting the blame on technology itself, the Socialists on capitalism. The Dystopian explanation of alienated labor is quite persuasive, its explanation of sexual alienation less persuasive, though still impressive, and its explanation of ecological crisis least persuasive. Dystopians seem justified in their fear of decreasing democracy and freedom or increasing dictatorship, but they seem wrong in construing this as a trend toward a Brave New World. And they are perhaps wrong in thinking that technology is growing continuously and is now getting out of hand, though their case here is intriguing. On balance, the Dystopian view is always thought-provoking, often insightful, but less often persuasive. Part three will explore whether the Socialists' view does better overall.

Notes

[1]Donella H. Meadows, Dennis L. Meadows, Jørgen Randers, and William H. Berens III, *The Limits to Growth* (New York: Universe Books, 1972), p. 34.

[2]Ibid., pp. 115–117.

[3]Robert E. Baldwin and Gerald M. Meier, *Economic Development: Theory, History, Policy* (New York: Wiley, 1957), pp. 115–116.

[4]Ibid., pp. 124–128.

[5]Albert O. Hirschman, *The Strategy of Economic Development* (New Haven: Yale University Press, 1958), pp. 176–182.

See also Simon Kuznets, *Modern Economic Growth: Rate, Structure, and Spread* (New Haven: Yale University Press, 1966).

[6]For example, "I have just scratched the surface of the problem of environmental deterioration, but I hope that I have at least convinced you that subtle ecological effects may be much more important than the obvious features of the problem. The causal chain of the deterioration is easily followed to its source. Too many cars, too many factories, too much detergent, too much pesticide, multiplying contrails, inadequate sewage treatment plants, too little water, too much carbon dioxide—all can be traced easily to *too many people*." Paul R. Ehrlich, *The Population Bomb* (New York: Ballantine, 1968), pp. 66–67; cf. on this the controversy between Paul Ehrlich and John P. Holdren, on the one hand, and on the other, Barry Commoner in *Bulletin of Atomic Scientists* (May 1972), pp. 16–27, 42–56.

[7]Teacher's manual for Paul R. Ehrlich and Anne H. Ehrlich, *Population, Resources, Environment* (San Francisco: Freeman, 1970), p. 18.

[8]From *Newsweek*, January 26, 1970, quoted in R. Guiseppi Slater, Doug Kitt, Dave Widelock, and Paul Kangos, *The Earth Belongs to the People* (San Francisco: People's Press, 1970), p. 15.

[9]John C. Esposito, *Vanishing Air* (New York: Grossman, 1970), p. 28.

[10]Paul A. Baran and Paul M. Sweezy, *Monopoly Capital* (New York: Monthly Review, 1966), pp. 135–138.

[11]Esposito, *Vanishing City*, pp. 44–47.

[12]Robert Fitch and Mary Oppenheimer, "Who Rules the Corporations," Part 2, *Socialist Revolution*, September-October, 1950, pp. 105–114; Part 3, *Socialist Revolution*, November-December 1970, pp. 47–57.

[13]Barry Commoner, *The Closing Circle* (New York: Knopf, 1971).

[14]Ibid., p. 144.

[15]Ibid.

[16]Ibid., pp. 259–266.

[17]Ibid., p. 182.

[18]John Kenneth Galbraith, *The New Industrial State* (New York: New American Library, 1967), pp. 24–25.

[19]Donella H. Meadows, Dennis L. Meadows, Jørgen Randers, and William H. Berens III, *The Limits to Growth* (New York: Universe Books, 1972), pp. 56–57.

[20]Committee on Resources and Man, *Resources and Man* (San Francisco: Freeman, 1969), p. 119. See also Meadows, et al., *Limits to Growth*, pp. 56–59.

[21]Paul R. Ehrlich and Anne H. Ehrlich, *Population, Resources, Environment*, 2nd ed. (San Francisco: Freeman, 1972), p. 72; G. Tyler Miller, Jr., *Replenish the Earth* (Belmont: Wadsworth, 1972), p. 121; *Scientific American*, 224, No. 3 (September, 1971), 42.

Part Three

THE SOCIALIST VIEW

11

Who Rule: Capitalists or Technocrats?

Socialism Defined

Socialism means many things to many people. Before we discuss the Socialist view of technology, therefore, we need to get a clear meaning of "Socialism."

On the simplest level, a Socialist is anyone who is committed to eliminating capitalist production systems and replacing them by socialist production systems. It is quite easy to specify what a capitalist production system is: capitalism is any system of production in which the goods produced, as well as the labor used to produce them, are traded in a (relatively) open market, and in which the means of production are owned and controlled by a small minority of nonproducers (the capitalists). There is considerably more confusion about the nature of socialist systems of production. Socialist systems are often defined as systems in which production is controlled by the state, or as systems with a primary commitment to welfare and economic equality. But these are really misconceptions of what the great Socialist thinkers had in mind. State management of the economy, as well as an elaborate system of welfare, are perfectly compatible both with capitalism, and with totalitarianism. But socialism, at least as conceived by its great spokespersons (such as Karl Marx and Pierre Joseph Proudhon) is incompatible with both capitalism and totalitarianism.

By a socialist system I mean any system in which the working class owns and controls the means of production. Where worker control does not exist, socialism does not exist. It is true, of course, that in socialist systems the state manages the economy, but this is because the working class controls the economy through the intermediary of the state. Any system in which state management of the economy is not under the direction of the working class fails to qualify as a socialist system. It is true also that socialist systems are committed to extensive welfare expenditures and to reduced inequality. However, any welfare handed down by paternalistic ruling elites to passive masses is not socialist welfare. And Socialists do not claim that socialist systems will generate complete wealth and income equality. Karl Marx himself says that in socialism workers will be paid according to how much they work and how skillful their work is.

Given this conception of socialism—which is the conception of the great Socialist thinkers—it is not obvious that there are any real socialist societies existing in the world today. Some societies which claim to be socialist (such as the Soviet Union) in all probability are not; that is, their economies are not really under the control of the working class.

Even within this narrow definition, however, there are a variety of Socialist theories. Socialists disagree on many things, such as the nature of the basic contradictions of capitalism, of the transition from capitalism to socialism, of economic decision making within socialism and of the role of the state within socialism. Is capitalism to be eliminated by revolution or by gradual reform? Should economic decision making under socialism be centralized or decentralized? Should state power be increased or decreased under socialism? Can socialist revolutions take place in backward countries? All these questions divide Socialists into hostile camps. The major distinction is between Socialists who claim to follow the thought of Karl Marx and those who do not. Marxists generally have a much more developed theory of capitalism and socialism than non-Marxist Socialists.

In the next three chapters, I will develop and, within limits, defend the Socialist views of technology and society. Though these views have certain weaknesses, they nonetheless are more plausible than the Utopian and Dystopian views. Socialists are fairly united and fairly systematic in their criticisms of the other views of the social role of technology. I will present some of the more important criticisms of Utopians and Dystopians shared by all Socialists (in chapters 11 and 12). I then will turn to the positive formulations by Socialists of the social role of technology (chapter 13). Unfortunately, Socialists are divided and somewhat inarticulate in their general theories of the social impact of technology. Indeed, among Socialists only Marxists have made any systematic attempt to develop a theory of this sort, and even their results are vague and sketchy. For this reason, I will focus almost exclusively on the thought of Karl Marx in presenting the positive Socialist view of the social role of technology.

Socialist Criticisms of Utopian and Dystopian Views

The Socialist view of technology and society is somewhat more complicated than the Utopian and Dystopian views. Socialists agree with both Utopians and Dystopians that technological change is a very important factor in social change. However, they do not go as far as many Utopians and Dystopians do to assert that technological change is the ultimate or primary factor in social change. They do not want to say that technology determines social change, though they insist that it has a strategic role in bringing about social transformations.

Socialists agree with Utopians that technology is a very important contributor to social progress, and even that it is necessary for social progress in the long run. There is no doubt that Socialists have a "pro" attitude on technology. Like the Utopians, they insist that the major social problems cannot be eliminated unless technology continues to be allowed to grow. However, Socialists deny that technological growth by itself can bring about social progress. Whether technology does in fact fulfill its progressive potential depends on who controls it; specifically, if a minority (such as the capitalist class) controls its development and use, then technology on balance can be expected to have a detrimental impact on the conditions of life of the subject classes (such as the industrial working class).

Along with the Dystopians, Socialists agree that the impact of technology in America is presently more regressive than progressive.

They insist with the Dystopians that American technology is creating more problems than it is resolving, and that it is worsening the quality of life. They maintain, again with the Dystopians, that the consequences of the use of American technology are growing worse with time. However, unlike the Dystopians, Socialists blame the capitalist class and not technology itself for the bad effects of the uses of technology; it is not the technology which is at fault but the people who control it.

Socialists are at odds with both Utopians and Dystopians on the following very basic question: who rules America and controls the uses of American technology? Socialists think that the capitalist class rules America and controls its technology, whereas many Utopians and Dystopians think that America is now a technocracy, ruled by technicians and scientists whose decisions are governed by the principles of technological rationality. Even those Utopians and Dystopians who allow that capitalists are the chief decision makers in America nonetheless deny that capitalists (or anyone else) really control the course of technological development. It is important then for Socialists to defend carefully their theory that capitalists are the American ruling class and the controllers of its technology. The Socialist arguments on this will be reviewed in this chapter.

Finally, Socialists agree with Utopians that the most basic social problems are economic problems, specifically the problem of scarcity. Along with Utopians, Socialists maintain that the elimination of economic scarcity will lead to the elimination of all other major social problems. Dystopians, as we have seen, do not agree with that. Many Dystopians indeed concede that technology is gradually leading toward the elimination of scarcity, but they insist that the attempt to eliminate scarcity is creating or intensifying many other problems. It is leading to political dictatorship, sexual repression, and alienated labor. Dystopians can therefore argue against the Utopian position without having to demonstrate that economic scarcity is not abating in America as technology is developing. But this is not true for Socialists; it is important for them to show that the use of technology is not leading to the gradual elimination of scarcity in capitalist America. We will see in chapter 12 whether Socialists can pull this off. Right now, however, let us move on to the question of who rules America and controls its technology.

Who Rules America?

How do Socialists make the case for their claim that the capitalist class (the class of primary owners of the means of production) is the American ruling class, and in virtue of this, the class which controls the development and uses of American technology? They operate with the basic working assumption that whoever controls the means of production controls society. They argue this in two stages. First, they attempt to show that the capitalist class, in virtue of its ownership of the means of production, controls the means of production. Second, they attempt to show that in virtue of its control of the means of production the capitalist class controls all the major political institutions (that is, it controls the state). In America, the means of production are organized within the corporate system, and the dominant political institutions are those constituting the federal government (as opposed to state and local governments). As applied to America, the Socialist strategy is to show that capitalists control the corporate system, and to show that, in virtue of this, they control the federal government. Let us begin with the first stage: who controls the corporations?

Who Controls the Corporations: The Technocracy Thesis

For many decades, almost everyone conceded to the Socialists that capitalists (the major owners of capital) controlled the major private corporations. This consensus began to fall apart by the 1930s when a number of scholars began to persuasively argue that nonowning managers and technicians within corporations were slowly and inevitably wresting power over corporations away from the owners of capital. Since then a large number of people have come to believe that employee manager-technicians (experts) and not owner-capitalists (such as stockholders) control the major corporations. Technocrats and not capitalists, we are told, hold sway over the corporate system. Let us refer to this thesis as the "technocracy thesis."

It is imperative for Socialists to disprove the technocracy thesis, but this is no easy matter. In chapter 4, when discussing the underlying assumptions of the Utopian view, I reformulated the major arguments in favor of the technocracy thesis. These arguments, it seemed to me, are very powerful. Before going on to the Socialist response, let me briefly summarize them.

There are two kinds of arguments usually put forth in favor of the technocracy thesis. On a more theoretical level, the proponents of the technocracy thesis attempt to demonstrate that the imperatives of modern technology require the transition from capitalist control to technician control. Modern technology being what it is, they maintain, there would be wholesale havoc and breakdown in the corporate system if the recommendations of experts regarding the disposition of that technology were more than occasionally overridden by the owners. The corporate system would be in disarray, it is said, if owners did not habitually rubber-stamp the proposals of manager-technicians. On a more empirical level, the proponents of the technocracy thesis attempt to demonstrate that the stockholders and financiers no longer have the economic wherewithal to exercise control over large corporations. This is presumably because the large blocks of stocks owned by single families or small groups in the individual corporations are slowly being eroded, broken up, or dispersed as corporations grow in size and as the major wealthy families and groups, under the pressures of growing membership, become less cohesive, and because corporations, now internally generating most of the required funds for investment, have little need for external finance in the form of loans or bonds. Hence, the evidence suggests that only in a very few large corporations is it the case that either a small group of stockholders has sufficient voting power or a few banks have sufficient credit power to exercise control over that corporation.[1]

The Socialist Response: Managers as Capitalists

Socialists have a number of options in response to the technocracy thesis, but the simplest is to straightforwardly deny that there is any difference in social class between outside stockholders or financiers and inside top managers. Socialists emphasize that top managers are themselves capitalists (though perhaps on a smaller scale) and play a capitalist role in the corporations that employ them.

Top managers are after all exceedingly wealthy; as a group, they easily belong to the top 1 percent in wealth and income. In 1963, the median income for top executive officers in major corporations was above $225,000. Top managers used a significant portion of this income to purchase stocks, especially in the corporations employing them. In 1963, the median stock income of chief executives was $64,000, approximately 41 percent of the median salary plus bonuses.[2] In 1959, the top managers owned an average of 1.9 percent of the total voting stock of their corporations. Though this holding is proportionately small, in absolute terms it amounts to a large sum of money and a high ownership stake for the manager. For example, a former chief executive officer of General Motors owned only 0.017 percent of outstanding stock, but at the time this was worth $3,917,000.[3]

It is still true that the wealth accruing to top managers, on the average, is puny compared to the wealth of the major outside stockholders or financiers, whose income comes mainly from their holdings and not their work. But there is no doubt that the interests of these small capitalist managers converge with those of the large outsider capitalist stockholders or financiers. Furthermore, it is a major objective of small capitalist managers to join the ranks of the large capitalists. Large and small socialize in the same circles, interpret the national interest in the same way, and struggle for the same goals.

Even if it were true that manager-technicians have wrested control over corporations from outside stockholders and financiers, it would not follow from this that noncapitalists have wrested power away from capitalists. Indeed, the reverse would be the case if the technicians who allegedly control corporations are all managers at the top of the organizational pyramids (that is, if they are chief executive officers or members of the board of directors).

Many supporters of the technocracy thesis, however, maintain that the controlling technicians are scattered all through the organizational pyramid and are not merely to be found at the top. According to John Kenneth Galbraith, for example, the technicians who participate in control of corporations include not only chief executive officers but also middle-level engineers, marketing researchers, systems analysts, and heads of research and development teams. His reasons for believing this are quite persuasive. If one concedes that expertise, rather than ownership of capital, is the primary instrument for exercising control over the corporation, then one must allow that any employee with an important and recognized kind of expertise shares proportionately in the exercise of power over the corporation, no matter where he or she may be located within the corporate pyramid. In Galbraith's words, "Any corporate decision will require information. Some power will then pass to the person or persons who have this information. If this knowledge is highly peculiar to themselves, then their power becomes very great."[4] Since sophisticated technical expertise is essentially specialized, one must concede that no small group of experts can exercise full control over the corporation. As expertise becomes more specialized and recondite, so should one expect that the number of technicians and managers participating in control will get larger and larger. If stockholders give up power to executives when they lack or fail to exercise managerial or overseeing skills then, by the same token, top executives give up some power to middle-level engineers when they lack or fail to exercise engineering skills. But it seems absurd to say of most middle-level experts and technicians in the corporation that they are capitalists or perform capitalist functions, and it is certainly outlandish to suggest that much of their income derives from stock ownership in the firm for which they work. So if it is admitted that the class of manager-technicians participating in corporate control includes middle-level personnel as well as chief executive officers, then it is no longer plausible to assert that the manager-technicians who do control corporations are capitalists.

Socialists must therefore do more to rebut the technocracy thesis than merely say that manager-technicians are themselves capitalists. This is true if one is referring exclusively to managers at the top of the organizational pyramid, but not so true if one is also referring to technicians at the middle levels of the organizational pyramid. What Socialists must do, in addition, is to demonstrate that outside owners and financiers have not lost control to the inside manager-technicians. This is not an easy task. Let us see how Socialists handle it.

The Socialist Response: Who Benefits from Corporate Activity?

We have little direct access to all that goes on inside the corporate system, so it is difficult to tell who really controls corporations. Corporations for us are like "black boxes"; since we do not have direct information on what goes on inside a black box, we can only attempt to determine what goes on inside by carefully observing what is put into the black box (the inputs) and what comes out of the black box (the outputs). Similarly in the case of corporations, we can only determine who controls them by analyzing the inputs into the corporate black box and the outputs emanating from it. Socialists can convince us that major owners of capital (rather than technicians) control corporations by showing us that major capitalists have especially privileged inputs into corporations and that major capitalists are especially favored by the outputs of corporations.

On the input side, Socialists will have to show that capitalists have the wherewithal to control corporations; that is, either capitalists have sufficiently concentrated ownership of stocks to control corporations or they provide corporations with a sufficient amount of credit (in the form of loans, bonds, etc.) to be able to dictate terms of policy. Generally, if Socialists can establish that most corporations' stocks are concentrated in few hands, or that they have strong institutional ties to banks and other creditors, or that they are controlled by other corporations with concentrated stock ownership or strong ties to banks, then Socialists will have gone a long way to prove that outside capitalists (and not inside manager-technicians) still control the corporations.

On the output side, Socialists will have to show not only that capitalists are the chief beneficiaries of corporations, but also that the relative benefits of capitalists from corporate activity have not diminished during the period of the alleged managerial revolution.

The analysis from the output side is the easiest, so let us deal with it first. Socialists can here argue very persuasively that capitalists simply would not benefit as lucratively as they in fact do from the normal activity of corporations if they were not in control. If manager-technicians had indeed wrested power over corporations from wealthy capitalists, then surely they would no longer be working to maximize the pecuniary gains of these wealthy capitalists. Conversely, we would expect that the share of the rich in the total individually owned wealth in American society would be decreasing, and/or that the value of the stock-derived wealth of the rich (their ownership wealth in corporations) would be decreasing relative to the value of their nonstock-derived wealth (such as from real estate), as they channeled their investments from corporate stocks to presumably more lucrative sources of income. But neither of these expectations turns out to be true.

With regard to the first, it has recently become well established that the distribution of wealth and income is not substantially different today than it was fifty years ago, though it has indeed fluctuated somewhat over the years. The top 1 percent own somewhere between 30 and 35 percent of the total wealth, as they did fifty years ago.[5] It is difficult to believe that the major owners of wealth have lost control over the major corporations during that period if their relative share in total wealth has not been affected negatively.

And, contrary to the second expectation, the top owners of wealth have displayed no tendency to take their money out of corporate stocks and to search out other avenues of investment; if anything the opposite has been the case. In 1922, the top 1 percent in wealth owned 18 percent of total real estate and 62 percent of all corporate stock. By 1953, their share in real estate had gone down to 13 percent, but their share in corporate stocks had gone up to 76 percent.[6]

So clearly on the output side, capitalists are just as well treated by the corporate system now as they were fifty years ago (before the supposed advent of the managerial revolution). This suggests that the managerial revolution has not really taken place.

The Socialist Response: Concentrated Stock Ownership

On the input side, Socialists must establish that capitalists have the wherewithal to control corporations. (It is not enough to show that they are the primary beneficiaries of corporate activity.) For any given corporation, capitalists have the wherewithal to control it if its stocks are concentrated in the hands of few owners, or if it is financially dependent on and institutionally tied to banks or if it is controlled by corporations meeting these first two conditions. Let us first consider the case of concentrated stock ownership.

Supporters of the technocracy thesis have made much of the alleged fact that stock ownership by individuals and families is much more diffused and unconcentrated than it used to be (see chapter 3), and certainly too diffused for it to allow ownership control by any small group of holders. But here it is difficult to get enough reliable data. Stock ownership can be concealed in a number of ways (such as in family trusts, foundations, holding companies, or fictitious corporations). Furthermore, corporations do not have to reveal who their stockholders are, nor do stockholders have to reveal which corporations they have holdings in. Also, the amount of stock usually required to control a corporation is often exaggerated (proponents of the technocracy thesis usually put it at 10 to 20 percent).

The only full and complete study of stock ownership in nonfinancial corporations in this country was made by the Senate's Temporary National Economic Committee (TNEC) in 1940. By use of the subpoena power, the TNEC was able to get information about stockholdings which was previously unavailable. The committee concluded that stockholdings still were very much concentrated. For example, it found that in 70 percent of the top 200 nonfinancial corporations one family, a small group of individuals, or some other corporation owned enough stock to exercise absolute majority control. It also found that the twenty largest stockholders of each of the top 200 firms held, on the average, one-third of the total stocks.[7] This would effectively put the greater majority of the top corporations under the control of individual and family stockholders.

Is the situation the same today? It is difficult to tell, since no thorough study since the TNEC has been commissioned. But if we take the owning of 5 percent of the total stock by a small group to be sufficient for control, then we can argue that at least one-third of the top 200 nonfinancial firms are controlled by a small group of individual or family stockholders. This certainly goes a long way to supporting the Socialist view. Firms such as Ford, Gulf, Alcoa, Sun Oil, and Du Pont are clearly under stockholder control by individuals, families, or small groups.[8]

The Socialist Response: Interlocks with Banks

But there are still a large number of firms (including the giants, General Motors, AT&T, and Standard Oil of New Jersey) in which no small group of individuals or families owns at least 5 percent of the stocks and thus has the wherewithal to control the corporation. For these nonfinancial corporations, Socialists must prove that they are controlled by other nonfinancial corporations or that they are dominated by banks or other financial institutions. In this age of conglomerates, there are a number of nonfinancial corporations controlled by other nonfinancial corporations. But this is not enough to cover all the corporations in which stock ownership is widely diffused. This leads to the question of the ties of these remaining corporations to banks.

Socialists have recently put much emphasis on what they take to be bank control over nonfinancial corporations. Much of their evidence has been meant to show that bankers have the appropriate inputs (that is, the wherewithal) to control major nonfinancial corporations. (They seem to assume that bank control over nonfinancial corporations entails capitalist control, perhaps because there is no doubt that major capitalists control the top banks or because banks themselves function primarily as institutional capitalists, as investors and money lenders.) Let us look at some of this evidence.

Clearly, the most important leverage that banks have over nonfinancial corporations is due to their immense resources for granting loans for investment. Corporations, of course, will use internal funds as much as possible to finance investment, but they have always had to depend on external funds. In 1968, for example, external finance (from banks, security houses, etc.) provided over 42 percent of all the funds needed for investment. And the dependence of corporations on external finance has apparently increased in the past decade or so (although fluctuations here are large and unpredictable).[9]

Financial institutions, such as banks, also own large blocks of stocks in nonfinancial corporations and manage even larger blocks owned by others; this gives them additional leverage over nonfinancial corporations. In 1952 financial institutions had discretionary power over approximately 20 percent of all corporate stocks; by 1965 they had discretionary power over 40 percent of all corporate stocks. (They owned 16 percent of the stocks in circulation and managed over 24 percent of the remaining stocks through their trust departments.)[10] Of the top 500 financial corporations, 147 have recently been found to have at least 5 percent of their stocks (a controlling share) owned by one of the top forty-nine banks. On the average, each of these banks held 5 percent of the stocks in 108 companies.[11]

No doubt, banks and other financial institutions can exercise considerable power over the nonfinancial corporations to which they have made loans or in which they own or manage stocks. This discretionary power is institutionalized through the device of interlocking directorships; that is, banks and other financial institutions arrange to have members of their board of directors sit on the boards of the corporations to which they have made loans or in which they own stocks.

Interlocking directorships are not scattered and diffused with each bank going its own way. They are highly concentrated and bring together large numbers of corporations into highly integrated networks. Major banks in a large city develop alliances among themselves, through interlocks and mutual stock ownership. As a group, and in conjunction with allied insurance companies, they exercise a considerable amount of discretionary power over the affairs of many major nonfinancial corporations. This creates a whole net of interrelated corporations whose behavior is orchestrated through their ties with major banks. These integrated systems are usually referred to as "interest groups." Each interest group is identified in terms of the major commercial center from which it emanates. There is a New York interest group, a Chicago interest group, a San Francisco interest group, a Pittsburgh interest group, and so on.[12] All in all, there are fifteen identifiable major interest groups, to which almost half of the top 250 nonfinancial corporations belong; it has been estimated that seventy-nine out of the biggest one hundred nonfinancial corporations, forty-six out of the fifty biggest banks, and eighteen out of the twenty biggest insurance companies belong to such interest groups.[13] The banks constitute the core of these interest groups, with the largest number of interlocks. Life insurance companies form the first ring around the core, utility companies the second ring, and industrial, transportation, and merchandising corporations constitute the outer ring.[14]

The New York group is by far the most awesome interest group. It consists of thirty-eight major corporations. At the center are six extremely large banks, of which Chase Manhattan, First National City (now known as Citibank), and Chemical are associated with the Rocke-feller subgroup interests, while Morgan Guaranty Trust and Bankers Trust are associated with the Morgan subgroup interests.[15] (The sixth bank, Manufacturers Hanover Trust, belongs to neither subgroup.) These six banks taken together have 25 percent of all trust assets in this country, and have 14 percent of all savings deposits.[16] Furthermore, these banks are allied with four major insurance companies; Metropoli-tan, Equitable Life, New York Life, and Mutual of New York.[17] These ten major finance institutions, insofar as they are integrated, represent a formidable source of credit and stockholder power. It should be no surprise that through their far-flung interlocks with nonfinancial corpo-rations they should exercise enormous power over the latter. And such indeed appears to be the case. Belonging to this New York interest group, and quite possibly dominated by the finance institutions operat-ing at the center, are six out of the top ten nonfinancial corporations, thirteen out of the top thirty, and sixteen out of the top sixty. Members of this group include such stalwarts as AT&T, Ford, U.S. Steel, Con-solidated Edison, General Electric, Chrysler, and Union Carbide.[18] This is not to say that the major New York banks, separately or in unison, necessarily control the above major nonfinancial corporations; it is to say rather that these banks have the proper inputs or where-withal, if not to exercise control automatically, at least to make a good fight for it.

In conclusion, Socialists can make a very good case against the technocracy thesis (the thesis that insider technicians control corpora-tions) and can persuasively defend their claim that major capitalists (inside or outside) control nonfinancial corporations. The Socialists' strategy is to attempt to demonstrate the four following propositions: most top managers are capitalists anyway; corporations reward the capitalist class today as well as they always have, and certainly much better than they do other groups (including technocrats); in a sig-nificant number of major nonfinancial corporations, stocks are still con-centrated in the hands of a few individuals or families; those nonfinan-cial corporations where stocks are less concentrated are either con-trolled by other nonfinancial corporations or financially dependent on, and institutionally tied to, financial institutions such as banks. Socialists can make a strong (although not foolproof) case for each of these prop-ositions. This makes their overall argument for capitalist control over corporations very strong, and proportionately weakens the initial plausibility of the technocracy thesis. All told, it seems we must reject the view that noncapitalist manager-technicians have wrested corporate control from the capitalists.

The Pluralist View

It is not too difficult, I think, for Socialists to defend the thesis that owners of capital control the major corporations; it is somewhat more difficult and complicated for them to defend the thesis that owners of capital control the United States federal government. Here Socialists run into the very popular pluralist view that no one group controls the federal government. Rather, according to the pluralist view, major political decisions of the federal government are a consequence of pressures from many groups, each competing with the other. This view concedes that capitalists have a good deal of influence over major political decisions; but so do labor unions, medical associations, and educational associations. No group gets its way all the time or loses all the time. The federal government is the principal arena of competition for the various groups and the locus at which a state of equilibrium is established between them. Capitalists, as a consequence of their power, get considerable benefits from the government; but as a consequence of the power of other groups they are subject to considerable unwanted constraints by the government. Such anyway is the pluralist view.[19]

In the remainder of this chapter, I will outline the Socialist answer to the pluralist view. A complete defense would require a lengthy presentation of all sorts of data, something that goes considerably beyond the scope of this book.

Private Governments

The federal government may seem so large and awesome that no group or class of persons, however rich and powerful, could have the resources to control or to monopolize influence over it. This may be true, but it should be remembered that members of the capitalist class (supposing that they control the major corporations) have awesome resources of their own with which to confront the government.

The major corporations are themselves governments of sorts. They are "private governments," insofar as they are accountable in their decisions not to the general public, but to their primary owners or creditors. In terms of their size and resources, these private governments dwarf the state and local "public governments" that surround them. The payroll of General Motors, for example, exceeds the combined payrolls of the state governments of New York, California, Illinois, Pennsylvania, Texas, and Ohio, and the annual revenues of Standard Oil of New Jersey exceed the local tax collections of the above six states, plus Wisconsin, Connecticut, and Massachusetts. The fifty largest corporations have three times as many persons working for them as the fifty states, and their combined sales are five times as high as the combined taxes collected by the fifty states.[20] According to the *Wall Street Journal*, "If a corporation's sales were to be equated with a nation's output of goods and services, then 51 of the world's top money powers would be international corporations, and only 49 would be countries."[21]

It should be no surprise, then, that major corporations, as private governments, settle or play a major role in settling many key social questions. These questions include the allocation of resources, the nature of products and the manner in which they are produced, the distribution of income, the extent of economic development or backwardness in many communities, the level and direction of investment, the direction of research, the shape of school curricula, and the direction of population flow (from country to city, from city to suburb).[22] Nor should it be a surprise that some giant corporations, such as United Fruit, ITT, and the major oil companies, can effectively create their own foreign policy.[23] Of course, once these corporations are integrated by finance institutions into large interest groups acting in cohesion, their discretionary authority is greatly multiplied.

The capitalists, then, when approaching the federal government, come well equipped. Do they use their equipment successfully?

Capitalist Access to the Federal Government

The federal government, like corporations, is to us something like a "black box": we are not privy to much of what goes on inside of it, and certainly we do not see enough of what goes on inside to tell who controls it. Again, to settle the issue of control, we have to look at the inputs and the outputs. On the input side, we must ask what sort of *access* capitalists have to the federal government. On the output side, we must ask what kinds of rewards capitalists garner from the federal government? If the capitalists have highly privileged access and receive highly disproportionate rewards, then it would be justifiable to claim that they control the federal government. Let us turn to the question of access first.

Capitalists, it has been argued, have highly privileged access to the federal government (and especially to the executive) through their disproportionate share in the membership of key positions and committees and through the disproportionate pressure that they can bring to bear on the federal government.

William Domhoff (author of *Who Rules America?* and *The Higher Circles*) has documented the ways in which capitalists gain membership, especially in the federal executive. He has shown that most of the key cabinet posts have been held by members of the capitalist class, or their functionaries, in the past forty years. He has pointed to all the in-house committees of the various executive departments which are populated almost exclusively by capitalists, such as the Business Advisory Committee (formerly of the Commerce Department) and the National Petroleum Council (of the Interior Department). He also has listed the policy and research institutes (such as the Council for Economic Development and the Brookings Institution) which are dominated by capitalists and their functionaries and which have such an important input into the federal executive.

Capitalist access to the federal legislative branch is achieved more by the exertion of external pressure rather than by inner membership. This pressure takes on many forms, such as organized lobbies, financial support of candidates, and control of the media. In terms of their resources and their unity of purpose, capitalists can usually marshall more effective lobbies than can their opponents. The effectiveness of capitalist lobbies is further reinforced by the fact that their function is to keep things as they are rather than to bring about significant changes. Opposing new legislation is usually easier than initiating and supporting it. (Business lobbies, of course, will support new legislation which, though bringing them small advantages, in no way changes the overall distribution of privileges.)

In their everyday decisions and actions, corporations automatically put pressure on the federal government, even in the absence of such pressures as lobbying, financial support of candidates, and media campaigns. No government can succeed in operating successfully in a crisis-free atmosphere when it does not have the confidence of business. The reason is obvious. When governments lose the confidence of business, this puts a damper on investment and leads to some form of recession, depression, or other economic crisis. Even socialist-oriented governments in liberal capitalist democracies have gone out of their way to put business at ease (by such methods as watering down their reform proposals). Salvatore Allende Gossens, the former president of Chile, did not go far enough in this direction and faced economic chaos throughout most of his unfinished term in office. Senator George McGovern, had he been elected president of the United States in 1972, no doubt would have been preoccupied with calming the fears of business.

Labor, on the other hand, does not have the same kind of automatic impact on governments. Other than the important role of helping to determine wages, labor unions have little to do with the everyday decisions involved in running the economy.

Consequently, a strong case can be made that capitalists have an especially privileged input into the federal government in the form of disproportionate membership and ability to apply direct and indirect pressure. Whether or not this entails control cannot be settled unless much more data are considered than have been looked at so far.

Capitalist Rewards From Public Government

The extent of capitalist influence or control over the federal government may also be measured by reference to the outputs of the federal government, namely, the extent of benefits accruing directly or indirectly to capitalists from the federal government.

At this point, it must be remembered that capitalists do not come directly to the government for most of their rewards and benefits; most of the wealth of capitalists, for example, is not disbursed by federal or state governments. It is in the private sector that the most important rewards are distributed, and in that sector (when working correctly) that the owners of capital are munificently compensated. The private sector is a power system with the capitalists as its ruling class; power in the private sector is used by capitalists for self-enrichment. As a private power system, the corporate sector is supported, overseen, and regulated by public power systems such as the federal government. The corporate sector is a private power system within a public power system. Since the capitalists get most of what they strive for from the private corporate sector, their only demand on public government is that it use its power to protect, nurture, and stimulate the private corporate system; to keep it healthy and working efficiently; to expand and rationalize its discretionary power over domestic and assorted foreign economies; and to help maintain, in the face of pressures from other groups (such as consumers and workers), the traditional privileges, powers, and benefits accruing to the capitalists from their participation in the private economy. If indeed public government does all this, then the public power system, though it theoretically has authority over the private power system, is in effect its instrument. If such is the case, then capitalists, in virtue of their control over the private power system, in effect have control over the public power system.[24]

Supporters of the pluralist view have of course argued that the above is not the case. As the story goes, the emerging twentieth-century welfare state has encroached on the economy by taking away significant portions of the capitalists' powers, privileges, and relative rewards. According to the pluralists, welfare state legislation has increasingly succeeded in subjecting the business community to external regulation by representatives of other groups (such as consumers) or by the spokesmen of the public interest. The regulatory agencies especially have been created to protect the general public or particular vulnerable groups from the potential abuses of large businesses. Pluralists also claim that welfare state legislation has in the long run brought about a net relative transfer of wealth and income from the rich to the poor and to the middle classes through the device of federal and state budgetary systems. Through the institution of the progressive tax system, the rich contribute disproportionately to the federal and state budgets; through the institution of transfer payments, the poor benefit disproportionately from budgetary expenditures of federal and state governments.

But the pluralist case is not as strong as it may initially appear.

Consider first the case of government regulation of business. It exists, no doubt. Still, there is now almost universal agreement that regulatory agencies regulate by serving the business interests which they are supposed to oversee. Business regulation by these agencies is in most cases just a form of self-regulation; agencies such as the Texas Railroad Commission and the Interstate Commerce Commission function as cartels for the businesses which they are supposed to regulate (such as oil and transportation); they set prices and settle disputes between the participant businesses. Where agency regulation is not business self-regulation, it is ineffective regulation, as in the case of the Federal Trade Commission. On this there is not much controversy (though some would want to qualify or tone down these judgments.)[25]

Further, it cannot be claimed that the budgetary practices of the welfare state have induced any relative loss in the capitalist share of total wealth or income. The overall tax structure has only a marginal effect on the distribution of wealth and income, and the bottom 20 percent do not have a greater share of total income after taxes than before.[26]

And it is not obvious that governmental budgetary expenditures favor lower income groups at the expense of higher income groups. Much of what is listed under public welfare in the federal budget is paid for by social security taxes, and a significant portion of public welfare is in the form of subsidies to rich farmers. Only a little over one-third of the federal public welfare budget is devoted to actual welfare transfers for the lower income groups. The public welfare budget in turn constitutes only one-third of the total federal budget. With respect to the remainder of the federal budget, it can be argued that large portions are actually subsidies for businesses; this seems true of much of the funds allocated to transportation, natural resource development, and research and development. It is especially true of the 40 percent or so of the federal budget allocated to defense. Defense spending stimulates the capitalist economy, is a source of huge profits for many corporations, and provides the military wherewithal for the protection of the interests of American corporations abroad. Capitalists even benefit from welfare transfers for the poor, since these help stabilize the economy by going down when the economy is going up and by going up when the economy is going down.[27]

The conclusion seems to be that, whether one looks at government regulation, the tax system, or federal budgetary outlays, the position of the capitalist class does not seem to have worsened as a consequence of the rise of the welfare state. The rich have as much power over their own fates and have as large a share in the total wealth as they had before the widespread development of federal regulation and welfare. If capitalists controlled the federal government before it became a welfare state, then surely they control it now.

Conclusion

Socialists claim that the capitalist class is to blame for the bad effects of technology in America. They argue that capitalists rule America and thus control the development and use of technology in America. Capitalists make the key decisions and set the primary goals for Americans. Presumably the goals of the capitalist class account for the uses of technology in America. If technology has been used extensively for mass manipulation and control, if its growth has been distorted by heavy governmental armaments spending, if it has intensified the alienation of workers and undermined the ecological balance, then, according to Socialists, all this is due to the fact that the interests of capitalists are the ruling interests of American society, not because of any tendency inherent in technology.

Is the Socialist view plausible? I have shown, I think, that it can be strongly supported by evidence. First, I summarized the evidence in support of the claim that capitalists control all the major corporations. Then I summarized the evidence in defense of the claim that capitalists, as controllers of the major corporations, control the federal government. In each case, I looked at the inputs and outputs (since power in corporations and in the federal government is not open to view). The questions asked were: Who has privileged access (on the input side) to major corporations and the federal government? Who is most richly rewarded (on the output side) by major corporations and the federal government? The answer to each question seems to be the capitalist class. Hence, Socialists seem to have a very good reason for saying that technology is not ultimately to blame in America for its ill effects and that those who control it (the capitalist class) are ultimately to blame.

Notes

[1]See chapter 4, pp. 42–55.

[2]Robert J. Larner, *Managerial Control and the Large Corporation* (New York: Dunellen, 1970), pp. 36–37.

[3]Ralph Miliband, "Professor Galbraith and American Capitalism," in David Mermelstein, ed., *Economics: Mainstream Readings and Radical Critiques* (New York: Random House, 1970), pp. 536–537; Galbriel Kolko, *Wealth and Power in America* (New York: Praeger, 1962), p. 66; John Kenneth Galbraith, *The New Industrial State* (New York: New American Library, 1967), p. 90, n. 8.

[5]William Domhoff, *Who Rules America?* (Englewood Cliffs, N.J.: Prentice-Hall, 1967), p. 43; Ferdinand Lundberg, *The Rich and the Super-Rich* (New York: Bantam, 1968), pp. 10–12; Howard P. Tuchman, *The Economics of the Rich* (New York: Random House, 1973), pp. 22–23.

[6]Domhoff, *Who Rules America?*, p. 45.

[7]Lundberg, *The Rich and the Super-Rich*, pp. 211–212.

[8]Miliband, "Professor Galbraith and American Capitalism," p. 535.

[9]Robert Fitch and Mary Oppenheimer, "Who Rules the Corporations?" Part 2, *Socialist Revolution*, No. 1, 5, 74; Peter C. Dooley, "The Interlocking Directorate," *American Economic Review*, 59 (June 1969), 318; *Radical Perspectives on the Economic Crisis of Monopoly Capitalism* (New York: Union for Radical Political Economics, 1975), pp. 22–23, 29, 32–33, 53–63.

[10]S. Menshikov, *Millionaires and Managers* (Moscow: Progress Publishers, 1969), pp. 162–163.

[11]Fitch and Oppenheimer, "Who Rules the Corporations?", Part 1, *Socialist Revolution*, 1, No. 4, 99.

[12]Dooley, "The Interlocking Directorate," pp. 319–322.

[13]Ibid., p. 319; Richard Pelton, "Who Really Rules America?" in *Progressive Labor*, 7 (February 1970), 21.

[14]Dooley, "The Interlocking Directorate," p. 320.

[15]Pelton, "Who Really Rules America?" pp. 17–19.

[16]Fitch and Oppenheimer, "Who Rules the Corporations?" Part 1, *Socialist Revolution*, 1, No. 4, 96–97.

[17]Dooley, "The Interlocking Directorate," p. 320.

[18]Ibid.

[19]See, for example, Robert A. Dahl, *Who Governs?* (New Haven: Yale University Press, 1961); Arnold M. Rose, *The Power Structure* (London: Oxford, 1967); Geraint Parry, *Political Elites* (New York: Praeger, 1969).

[20]Andrew Hacker, "A Country Called 'Corporate America,'" *New York Times Magazine*, July 3, 1966, pp. 8ff.

[21]Quoted from Austin *American-Statesman*, July 21, 1973, p. A5.

[22]Hacker, "A Country Called Corporate America"; see also Andrew Hacker, "Power To Do What?" in William E. Connolly, *The Bias of Pluralism* (New York: Atherton, 1969), pp. 67–81.

[23]See Robert Engler, *The Politics of Oil* (Chicago: University of Chicago Press, 1961); *The American Oil Industry* (New York: Marine Engineers' Beneficial Association, 1973); Anthony Sampson, *The Sovereign State of ITT* (New York: Stein and Day, 1973).

[24]C. B. Macpherson, *The Real World of Democracy* (London: Oxford, 1966), pp. 1–11.

[25]Engler, *Politics of Oil*; Edward F. Cox, Robert C. Fellmeth, John E. Schultz, *Nader's Raiders* (New York: Grove Press, 1969); Robert Fellmeth, *The Interstate Commerce Commission* (New York: Grossman, 1970); Grant McConnell, *American Power and American Democracy* (New York: Random House, 1966).

[26]Herman P. Miller, *Rich Man, Poor Man* (New York: Crowell, 1971), p. 16; Philip M. Stern, *The Rape of the Taxpayer* (New York: Random House, 1973), pp. 24–25, 206–211.

[27]James O'Connor, *The Fiscal Crisis of the State* (New York: St. Martin's, 1973), pp. 97–178; S. M. Miller and Pamela Roby, *The Future of Inequality*, (New York: Basic Books, 1970), p. 165; Michael Reich and David Finkelhor, "The Military Industrial Complex: No Way Out," in Tom Christoffel, David Finkelhor, and Dan Gilbarg, eds., *Up Against the American Myth* (New York: Holt, Rinehart, and Winston, 1970), pp. 73–109; Harry Magdoff, *The Age of Imperialism* (New York: Monthly Review, 1969).

12

Capitalism, Technological Growth, and the Elimination of Poverty

Utopians, Socialists, and the Problem of Scarcity

In their heyday, Utopians seemed to think that continued technological growth would lead to the end of scarcity in America. Socialists disagree that technological growth, all by itself, can do that. They do contend, of course, that scarcity should and can be eliminated and that technological growth is necessary for that; they simply deny that technology is sufficient to accomplish it. They insist that technological growth in capitalist countries does not lead to any sustained and significant reductions in the level of economic scarcity. Against the Utopians, therefore, they would argue that increasing affluence in America has not been accompanied by decreasing scarcity as technology has continued to develop. Can they persuasively pull this argument off? I think so.

Growing Wants, Ecological Breakdown, and Imperialism

Admittedly, in this century the record of American capitalism in dealing with the problem of scarcity has not been good, despite dramatic increases in the gross national product per capita. As the economy has continued to grow, so have the wants of consumers. Growth in the relative satisfaction of consumer wants, if it has taken place at all, has not kept up with the growth of the economy. Meanwhile, increasing production has been partially neutralized by the depletion of non-renewable resources and renewable free goods (such as clean air and water).[1] Everything else being equal, if wants continue to grow and renewable and nonrenewable natural goods continue to be depleted, then scarcity will increase.

America, in attempting to increase its total product, has exacerbated the scarcity in third world countries. We have already noted the extent to which the United States has been disproportionately exploiting the natural resources of other (especially third world) countries in order to keep its economy alive and growing.[2] But it has also been depleting the liquid assets (money) of these countries as well. Generally, American firms in third world countries siphon out more funds from these countries (such as in profits and interest on loans) than they bring in (such as investments).[3] Whatever decreases in scarcity the United States may have experienced may have been neutralized by the increases in scarcity it has brought about in third world countries.

These are all matters to which I have alluded in previous chapters. But so far I have said nothing about poverty, the most tragic form of economic scarcity. Certainly the economic scarcity experienced by the poor is more serious and reprehensible than that experienced by compulsive consumers who always want more than then have. If American capitalism were consistently decreasing the amount of poverty within its borders and was headed toward the elimination of poverty in general, it would be registering gains of the most important and impressive sort in the reduction of scarcity. The elimination of poverty would be a victory over scarcity of unprecedented proportion (even though by itself it would not constitute the elimination of scarcity).

It appears at first glance that the incidence of poverty in America has gradually been decreasing as technology has continued to develop. It is this apparent trend which has buoyed the Utopians' predictions of a future society in which all poverty and deprivation has been eradicated. It is this apparent trend which also, in the decades following the depression, did much to undermine the intellectual credentials of Socialists. (Karl Marx had predicted increasing misery for the working class, but the economic lot of the working class seems to have been consistently improving.) It is here that the confrontation between Socialists and Utopians is the sharpest. Socialists must show that the incidence of poverty in America has not gone down (or has only decreased insignificantly) in this century. But here they must undermine a very persuasive Utopian argument embodied in official views about poverty. Let us look at that Utopian argument first.

Technological Growth and the Decline of Poverty

Has technological growth in twentieth-century America led to continuous decreases in the incidence of poverty? Utopians can argue quite forcefully that it has. Their argument can be formulated as follows:

1. American per capita income has enjoyed a significant and sustained growth during this century, primarily as a consequence of sustained technological growth
2. The per capita real income of lower economic groups during this century has been increasing at the same pace as the national average
3. As the real per capita incomes of lower economic groups increases, the incidence of poverty among these groups decreases proportionately
4. Conclusion: The incidence of poverty in America has been decreasing significantly and continually during this century, primarily as a consequence of sustained technological growth

The conclusion of this argument obviously follows from the premises. Socialists can thus only criticize this argument by attacking one of the premises. But each of the above premises seems at first blush to be true. In defense of the first premise, one may point to the fact that per capita income in America (in 1968 dollars) has increased from $4,700 in 1929, to $5,800 in 1947, to $7,400 in 1962, and to $8,900 in 1968.[4] The second premise is based on statistics showing that the relative income shares of the various income groups (such as, from the top 20 percent of income receivers to the lowest 20 percent) have only changed marginally in this century. These first two premises are hardly questionable.

This leaves only the third premise, which is somewhat more controversial. This premise assumes that the demarcation between the poor and the nonpoor is established by reference to a fixed, unchanging real income line. This is the position taken by the Social Security Administration (hereon referred to as the "SSA") in establishing the official government measure of poverty. According to the SSA, any family of four is, was, or will be in poverty if it is, was, or will be receiving a yearly income of less than $3,100 in constant 1963 dollars or, equivalently, a yearly income of less than $4,000 in constant 1970 dollars. ($4,000 in 1970 had just the same value as $3,100 in 1963.) From year to year, the only adjustment that the SSA makes in the poverty income line is for inflation; the poverty line is not raised from year to year except to allow for cost of living increases.[5]

The SSA gets its poverty income line by multiplying by three the value of the minimal nutritionally adequate food budget, as based on the economy food plan of the Department of Agriculture. (It assumes that food costs are approximately one-third of all costs necessary for the satisfaction of subsistence needs.)[6]

Clearly, the SSA measure supports the third premise, which says that the rate of poverty goes down proportionately as the real incomes of lower income groups go up. As real incomes go up across the board, the incidence of families of four earning less than $3,100 in 1963 dollars, and hence less than the SSA poverty income line, goes down proportionately. Hence, given the truth of the first two premises (namely, that in America real per capita income is continually going up while inequality remains the same), the application of the SSA measure leads us to conclude that the rate of poverty is continually and significantly decreasing. Indeed, the percentage of persons falling below the SSA poverty line has decreased from 59 percent in 1929, to 32 percent in 1947, to 20 percent in 1963, and to 12.6 percent in 1970.[7] During the brief life of Johnson's "War on Poverty," the SSA calculates that the incidence of poverty went down from one-fifth to one-eighth of the American population. The SSA measure obviously supports the Utopian position.

It is imperative for Socialists, therefore, to successfully undercut and criticize the SSA measure of poverty. Otherwise, Utopians will have been proven right in saying that technological growth in America leads to dramatic decreases in the incidence of poverty and that this growth is ultimately pointing toward the virtual elimination of poverty. This would be devastating for the Socialist position.

It is not enough here for Socialists merely to argue that the SSA poverty income line is too low. By establishing that a higher poverty income line is more correct (say, $5,000 in 1963 dollars for a family of four). Socialists will not have proven what they need to prove. All they will have been able to prove thereby is that the real rate of poverty, at any given time, is much higher than that projected by the SSA; they will not have been able to prove that the rate of poverty has not been declining significantly. It is therefore not enough for Socialists to argue about the specifics of the SSA package; what they must attack is the general conception of poverty, or the general approach to poverty, which underlies the SSA measure of poverty, and other measures like it. They must provide an alternative general approach to, or conception of, poverty.

The SSA measure embodies what I shall call the fixed absolute income approach to poverty. I shall formulate it, criticize it, and then consider other general approaches which Socialists might support in its place. These alternative approaches I shall label the variable relative income approach and the variable absolute income approach. Notice that these different approaches are generated by combining the opposites (fixed-variable and absolute-relative) in different ways. (A fourth possible combination, the fixed relative income approach, is altogether implausible.)

Poverty in America: The Fixed Absolute Income Approach

Let us begin by stipulating that anyone is poor who lacks the economic wherewithal necessary for the satisfaction of his or her subsistence needs. This is a position with which I think anyone can agree. However, there is much contention about the way in which the expressions "economic wherewithal" and "subsistence needs" are to be interpreted or applied. What is to count as the lack of economic wherewithal? What is to count as a subsistence need? The different answers to these questions generate different conceptions of poverty.

The approach most conducive to the Utopian position and which supports the SSA measure is the fixed absolute income approach. According to it, something is a subsistence need if and only if it is a biological need. A biological need is any need does not come into being as a consequence of conditioning, learning, or socialization, and which is required for the satisfaction of some inherited want or drive, for the actualization of some inherited capacity, or for the fulfillment of some organ function. People, for example, have a biological need for certain nutrients (such as proteins and carbohydrates); they have a biological need to maintain certain conditions of equilibrium in their bodies (such as temperature and water composition).

The proponents of the SSA measure seem to assume that there is a large core of biological needs shared by all, or nearly all, humans. Insofar as subsistence needs are identified by them with biological needs, subsistence needs are assumed by them to remain the same from society to society, place to place, and time to time. Consequently, they assume the standards distinguishing poverty from nonpoverty, insofar as they are formulated by reference to the set of subsistence needs, will be constant over time and place. That is, the proponents of the SSA measure assume that the standards distinguishing poverty from nonpoverty are absolute rather than culturally or temporally relative; the same standards hold everywhere and at every time. The general approach of the SSA is an absolute, rather than a relative, approach to measuring poverty.

The satisfaction of these culturally and temporally invariant needs requires a certain amount of consumable goods and services (such as food, shelter, clothing, education, transportation, medicine, security, and recreation). According to the SSA, the poor are those who lack the purchasing power for acquiring these minimal goods and services. Since purchasing power is assumed to be a function of real income, the poor are those whose real income is substantially inadequate for purchasing the market basket containing those goods and services necessary for the satisfaction of their biological needs. It is assumed that the size or value (or, equivalently, the real cost) of this market basket remains more or less constant over time and place, and hence that the real income just sufficient for purchasing it remains more or less constant over time and place. From this it follows that the line separating the poor from the nonpoor is indeed a fixed income line, determined by culturally and temporally invariant (or absolute) standards. Such is the fixed absolute income approach to poverty which appears to buttress the SSA measure of poverty.

In effect, the fixed absolute income approach embodied in the SSA measure of poverty unqualifiedly supports invariance in the measurement of poverty. It assumes that the standards for demarcating poverty from nonpoverty are invariant with respect to culture and time; this is what makes it an *absolute* approach. It further assumes that the real incomes (measured in terms of goods and services) needed to satisfy these standards are invariant with respect to culture and time; this is what makes it a fixed income approach. Finally, the standards are assumed to be invariant because subsistence needs (as biological needs) are assumed to be invariant.

It clearly follows from the fixed absolute income approach that if per capita income grows while the level of inequality remains the same (as has been the case in America during this century), then the rate of poverty will decline proportionately. So the fixed absolute income approach can be used to support the SSA measure, and therewith the Utopian position. It can therefore be used to undercut the Socialist position. Socialists must provide an alternative approach to the fixed absolute approach to poverty. Most Socialists and their liberal allies on this issue put forth a variable relative income approach. Let us examine this next.

Poverty in America: The Variable Relative Income Approach

It is obviously the SSA's insistence on the fixity of the real poverty income line which leads it to the Utopian view that poverty will continue to decrease in America as the capitalist economy grows. Socialists and their liberal allies insist that the real poverty income line must be upgraded proportionately as the capitalist economy grows. They are thus in support of a variable income approach. That is, they think that the market basket of subsistence goods (required for being above the poverty line) will grow as the capitalist economy grows. But what can justify this? Why should the amount of goods used to separate poverty from nonpoverty go up just because the economy produces more? Why should we continually get fussier about who we are to count as the nonpoor? Are we not weakening the condemnatory force of the expression "is poor" by diluting the standards, or diluting the measures, for determining who is poor? What alternative conception of poverty will justify the upgrading of the poverty income line with the growth of the capitalist economy?

The most obvious way to support a *variable* income approach is by appealing to some relative standards approach. That is, one can most straightforwardly defend the practice of continually upgrading the poverty income line in a growing capitalist economy by claiming that subsistence needs are culturally and temporally variant and that they will grow as the capitalist economy grows. This seems to have been Karl Marx's view:

> The worker's natural wants, such as food, clothing, fuel, and housing, vary according to climatic and other physical conditions of his country. . . . On the other hand the number and extent of his socially necessary wants . . . are themselves the product of historical development and depend, therefore, to a great extent on the degree of civilization of a country.[8]

Presumably, according to Marx, the class of subsistence needs includes not only biological needs but also some historically created needs. At least in capitalist societies, the class of historically created subsistence needs presumably grows as per capita incomes increase across the board. This also seems to be the view of most contemporary Marxists, such as Paul Baran, Paul Sweezy, and Ernest Mandel.[9]

This view, however, is not without its difficulties. Once we include among subsistence needs those needs which are nonbiological and historically created, we run into the difficulties of distinguishing between subsistence and nonsubsistence needs. Is any strongly felt need a subsistence need? If someone feels very deprived for not having a sports car like his friends do, is he thereby poor? Suppose that he feels just as poor and deprived as does the head of a ghetto family? Is he thereby just as poor? This seems wrong; there is more to being poor than simply feeling poor.

This difficulty, however, can be met in the following straightforward fashion. In any society, there is a standard view of what is to count as a minimally decent life. A decent life is a life that persons with average income can afford, with some leeway for savings and luxury goods. In this view, the subsistence needs of a given society are precisely those needs which must be satisfied if one is to live the standard decent life of that society. Anyone is poor, therefore, whose income is inadequate to purchase those goods and services necessary for the living of a minimally decent life; anyone is poor whose income is substantially below the appropriately designated average income.

Any appropriately designated average income will inevitably go up as per capita income goes up across the board. The standard for a minimally decent life will hence inevitably increase with across-the-board increases in per capita income. In a growing economy, the incidence of poverty will not decrease if there is no decrease in the percentage of persons receiving substantially less than the growing, appropriately designated average income. That is, in a growing economy the incidence of poverty will not decrease if there is no decrease in the percentage of persons receiving substantially less than the income necessary for meeting the continually rising standards for decent living. On this, consider the words of H. P. Miller:

> The essential fallacy of the fixed poverty line is that it fails to recognize the relative nature of "needs." The poor will not be satisfied with a given level of living year after year when the levels of those around them are going up at the rate of about 3 percent per year. Oldtimers may harken back to the "good old days" when people were happy without electricity, flush toilets, automobiles, and television sets; but they must also realize that once it becomes possible for all to have these "luxuries," they will be demanded and will quickly assume the status of "needs."[10]

Or, in the words of an economic report to the president:

> As average incomes rise, society amends its assessment of basic needs. Individuals who cannot afford more than a small fraction of the items enjoyed by the majority are likely to feel deprived. Consequently, an absolute standard that seems appropriate today will inevitably be rejected tomorrow, just as we now reject poverty definitions appropriate a century ago.[11]

The approach to poverty just presented as an alternative to the fixed absolute income approach may be labeled the variable relative income approach. According to it, the subsistence needs which provide the standards for demarcating the poor from the nonpoor are relative to time and place; consequently, the poverty income line will vary in accordance with time and place. Unlike the fixed absolute income approach, the variable relative income approach when applied to a growing capitalist economy does not support the Utopian view that the incidence of poverty is continually decreasing as per capita income is continually increasing. On the contrary, insofar as it has been established by critics of American capitalism that there has been in the long run no decrease in the extent of economic inequality in America (or in other capitalist countries), then the variable relative income approach supports the Socialist claim that there has been, in the long run, no significant decreases in the incidence of poverty in America or other capitalist countries. Obviously, this is because (as the most plausible version of the variable income approach) there is a direct correlation between the extent of poverty in a given society and the extent of inequality in that society. That is, there is a direct correlation between the incidence of poverty and the proportion of persons making less than some appropriate average income. This is why many liberal and Socialist critics of the way in which America has coped with the problem of poverty tend to speak interchangeably of poverty and inequality. The Socialist David Mermelstein exhibits this most explicitly:

> Ultimately, poverty is a condition of life, the real meaning of which is socially defined—*when there are no rich, there can be no poor.* By setting limits which allow poor persons to purchase television sets, officialdom believes that it has made due allowances for this social content of poverty. This is not so. It merely creates an upward adjustment to the boundary line of poverty. In a relatively rich society such as the United States, poverty is as much psychological as it is physical, in the sense that *an individual evaluates his life by contrasting it with others in that society. Therefore, poverty will persist indefinitely as long as income and wealth remain sharply unequal.* Changes must take place in these distributions of income and wealth if poverty is to be eradicated.[12]

Suppose, for example, that it is agreed that any family is poor which receives less than half the median family income (as has been proposed by Victor Fuchs). So determined, the poverty line for families in America went up from $2,100 in 1947 to $3,400 in 1965. Nonetheless, the incidence of poverty among families went up from 18.9 percent in 1947 to 20 percent in 1965; this clearly supports the Socialist position.[13]

Criticisms of These Two Approaches

For the moment, at any rate, the confrontation between the Utopian and Socialist views on poverty is reduced to the confrontation between the fixed absolute income and the variable relative income approaches to poverty. Which of these is most defensible? First, we may ask which of these coheres best with our intuitions. The surprising answer is that neither coheres well with our intuitions, and on these grounds each must be rejected.

Consider first the fixed absolute income approach. It generates conclusions and predictions which are in gross disagreement with our perceptions of the variations in the incidence of poverty from time to time and from culture to culture. For example, within the framework of an industrial growth economy a fixed income measure developed in the year Y to apply to the year Y, will tend to overestimate the numbers of the poor when it is applied to the years preceding Y, and will tend to underestimate the numbers of the poor when applied to years following Y. The half-century work of the British sociologist B. S. Rowntree nicely illustrates this point. Rowntree made studies of the incidence of poverty in the city of York in the years 1899, 1936, and 1950. By appeal to a well-defined measure, he concluded in 1899 that 28 percent of the York population was poor. He came back in 1936, upgraded his measure, and found that 17 percent of the York population was poor. When he returned in 1950, he further upgraded his measure and again found that a sizable portion of the York population was poor. Had he used the 1899 measure in 1936, he would have found only 4 percent of the population to be poor. By applying the 1899 measure in 1950, he would have found virtually no poverty in York; with the 1936 measure he would have concluded that in 1950 only 2.7 percent of the York population was poor.[14] But these claims surely would have conflicted with the perceptions of anyone who had carefully observed the York scene in those years. On the other hand, had the 1950 poverty income measure been applied in 1899, it surely would have led to some unintuitive finding, for example, that over 70 percent of the York population was poor. Another illustration: in 1936 Franklin Roosevelt said that one-third of the country was "ill-housed, ill-clad, ill-nourished." If he was right, the poverty income line in 1936 was at $2,000 (in 1970 dollars). If the same measure had been used in 1970, then only 4.6 percent of the American population would have been construed as poor.[15] The Roosevelt measure was liberal when used in his time, but it had to be upgraded in 1970 in order to be in harmony with the contemporary perceptions of poverty.

Similar difficulties confront a fixed income measure when applied to different regions or cultures. A fixed income measure of poverty formulated in some region R to apply to region R, (say, Ireland) will tend to overestimate the numbers of the poor when transposed to some region less developed economically than R (say, Indonesia), and will tend to underestimate the numbers of the poor when transposed to some region more developed than R (say, the United States).

It appears that no fixed income approach can cohere without perceptions of the variations of poverty over space and time. Unfortunately, no relative income approach will succeed in this respect either, although for opposite reasons. Consider, for example, the view that the poverty income line should be half the median income. This leads to patently absurd conclusions for societies that are both egalitarian and economically backward, as well as for societies that are both inegalitarian and highly affluent. As an illustration, take a preindustrial society whose median family income is $80 per year and 1 percent of whose families earn less than the median income. As we note widespread malnutrition, disease, winter discomfort, and insecurity, we might rationally estimate that over half the population is poor. Still, the relative income criterion introduced above would sanction the odd conclusion that only 1 percent of the population is poor, and hence that poverty has been virtually eliminated in that society. Or, take a futuristic postindustrial society whose median family income is $40,000 in 1970 dollars, and 20 percent of whose families receive an income between $16,000 and $20,000. These 20 percent may desperately want things which they cannot afford (such as yachts and palatial homes). They may be compulsive consumers, but surely they are not poor. And yet the relative income criterion introduced above would sanction the conclusion that these 20 percent of families are all poor. Here again the relative income approach clashes with our intuitions. Generally, to the extent that a society is egalitarian and indigent, to that extent do relative income approaches tend to underestimate the numbers of the poor. To the extent that a society is affluent and inegalitarian, to that extent do they tend to overestimate the numbers of the poor. This is true particularly for any approach which looks to inequality for the criterion, or the major cause, of poverty.

Poverty in America: The Variable Absolute Income Approach

It follows that no fixed income approach and no relative income approach will work. This means that we must reject the fixed absolute income approach presupposed by the SSA (and supporting the Utopian view) as well as the variable relative income approach presupposed by Socialists and some of their liberal allies. This leaves us with only one alternative, the variable absolute income approach. According to it, the subsistence needs providing standards for demarcating poverty from nonpoverty are culturally and temporally invariant, and yet the real costs for satisying these subsistence needs will fluctuate considerably from society to society and from economic stage to economic stage. Can such an approach be defended? And if so, can it help resolve the controversy between Socialists and Utopians on changes in the rate of poverty in America? On both counts I think it can. Indeed, not only does it cohere with our perceptions of the variations of poverty over time and place, but it also explains why these perceptions are in fact correct. Though in the abstract it is neutral on the controversy between Socialists and Utopians, it does tend to support the Socialist view when conjoined with fairly plausible claims concerning recent trends in advanced capitalism.

We can agree that subsistence needs, as biological needs, are culturally and temporarily invariant. Nonetheless, we can still allow that the contents of the market basket that just satisfy these invariant needs, and hence the real income just sufficient for avoiding poverty, will vary quite dramatically from society to society and time to time. We can even allow for the possibility that in some societies the minimal income necessary for satisfying these invariant needs will increase as the economy grows. The reason for this is fairly obvious. Though invariantly present from culture to culture, subsistence needs can be satisfied in a variety of ways from culture to culture. Indeed, socioeconomic systems can be differentiated in terms of the sorts of opportunities and means which they provide for the satisfaction of biological needs, and in terms of the obstacles which they put up. The means or instruments provided by one socioeconomic system for satisfying biological needs may be more costly to appropriate than those provided by another because they are more complicated or inferior; or because they require more resources or are otherwise more costly to produce; or because they satisfy a whole variety of nonsubsistence needs at the same time that they satisfy subsistence needs; or because the obstacles to the satisfaction of biological needs generated by one socioeconomic system may be more expensive to overcome than those generated by another. For these reasons, the costs of staying out of poverty in one system may be higher than in another, and so the poverty income line in one system may be higher than that in another. Furthermore, it is possible that there are socioeconomic systems which, as they grow economically, create increasingly more expensive instruments or means for satisfying biological needs and create increasingly more plentiful and more expensive obstacles to the satisfaction of these needs. In these systems, the costs of staying out of poverty, and hence the real poverty income line, will continually rise.

Within the framework of a variable absolute income approach, can it be argued persuasively, in defense of the Socialist position, that advanced capitalist countries, particularly America, continually tend to raise the costs of avoiding poverty as they grow economically. Can it, in other words, be argued that modern capitalist countries, particularly America, tend (in order to satisfy biological needs as they grow economically) to create more costly instruments for their citizens to appropriate and more costly obstacles for them to overcome? I think it can. For it can be maintained with some plausibility that modern capitalism supports the following trends which continually add to the costs of staying out of poverty: increasing urbanization, growing city ghettoes, continued expansion of the monopoly and oligopoly sectors, continued expansion of the welfare state, sustained technological growth, and maintenance of a constant level of economic inequality. Consider how each of these trends contributes to increasing costs for satisfying invariant biological needs.

INCREASING URBANIZATION

Urban living adds to the obstacles to the satisfaction of biological needs. There are health hazards (such as garbage, human waste, pollution, and overcrowding) and safety hazards (such as crime, fire, and heavy traffic). These require the provision of a variety of services and goods not required, or required to a lesser extent, in rural environments. Housing in the city can no longer be built just to keep out the elements; it must satisfy complex safety, sanitation, and security standards. Cities have no natural recreational environments and must institute them. And city living greatly increases the need for transportation.

GROWING CITY GHETTOES

The ghetto presents added obstacles to the satisfaction of biological needs. Pollution and crime are worse; population is denser; stress is higher; health hazards are greater. The services provided to cope with these problems are uniformly inadequate. Transportation systems are poor and jobs far away. Recreational facilities are scarcer. Foods and durables, provided mainly by small shops, are more expensive.[16]

THE CONTINUED EXPANSION OF THE MONOPOLY AND OLIGOPOLY SECTORS

Monopolization and oligopolization increase the real costs of commodities through planned obsolescence, through increased advertising, and through intense attempts at product differentiation.

THE CONTINUED EXPANSION OF THE WELFARE STATE

The emergence of the welfare state is supposed to have been a boon to the lower economic strata. It has actually added to the real costs of staying out of poverty. The new expenditures of the welfare state have been funded either by raising regressive taxes (such as sales and property taxes) or by adding regressive elements to the progressive income tax. Between 1962 and 1968, social security taxes went up 60 percent for the lowest income groups, sales taxes went up 30 percent, and property taxes went up 48 percent. And the federal income tax since the New Deal has continued to encroach on lower real incomes. And a very large part of tax-funded expenditures (such as for defense, roads, higher education, research and development), are much more conducive to the interests of upper-income strata than they are to the interests of lower-income strata (as I have argued previously).[17]

UNCHANGING INEQUALITY IN A GROWING ECONOMY

The standards for production in inegalitarian capitalist market societies seem to be set by the consumption habits of the more affluent. Capitalist systems, in determining which sorts of goods or services to produce for the satisfaction of biological needs, will tend to produce the sorts of goods or services preferred by the more affluent. They will stress the production of beef to satisfy protein needs, of cars and airplanes to satisfy transportation needs, and of television sets to satisfy recreational needs. But the goods or services preferred by the more affluent for the satisfaction of biological needs will tend to be more costly to produce and to appropriate than the alternatives—the car is more costly than mass transportation, beef more costly than nonmeat proteins, and television more costly than informal neighborhood entertainment. In part, this is because the goods and services preferred by the more affluent for satisfying biological needs tend at the same time to provide many nonnecessary amenities. The automobile, for example, is not only for some an indispensable means of transportation to jobs, but is also an instrument of escape, a source of thrills, a status symbol, and a hideaway for teenage lovers. Thus, the more unequal a capitalist market society is, the more costly are the means for satisfying biological needs. As the society grows economically, and its rich get richer in the absence of any reduction in income inequality, then the commodities meant for the satisfaction of biological needs, suited as they are for the tastes of the more affluent, will tend to become increasingly more costly to produce and to appropriate.

CONTINUED TECHNOLOGICAL GROWTH

Technological growth, at least within capitalism, continually changes and sometimes upgrades the requirements for job training. It tends to transform lower-skilled jobs into meaningless, repetitious tasks, and it contributes to the spread of external diseconomies (such as pollution, urban blight, noise, and stress).

To sum up, within the framework of a variable absolute income approach, one can argue quite plausibly for the Socialist position on poverty in the following way:

In advanced capitalist societies, there are sustained trends toward increasing urbanization, ghettoization, monopolization and oligopolization, welfarism, and technological growth, and no trend toward the reduction of income inequalities.

But the costs of staying out of poverty (i.e., the costs of satisfying invariant subsistence needs) will grow as the economy grows, wherever there exists increasing urbanization, ghettoization, monopolization, welfarism, growing technology, and no improvement in the distribution of income.

Therefore, in advanced capitalist societies, the costs of staying out of poverty (i.e., of satisfying invariant subsistence needs) grow as the economy grows. Consequently, there is no long term tendency in advanced capitalist societies for the incidence of poverty to decrease significantly as the economy grows.

Conclusion

Utopians maintain that as technology continues to grow the rate of poverty will continue to decline in America, and will ultimately be reduced to zero. Socialists disagree. They see little progress in the reduction of the rate of poverty; and they think that as long as capitalism maintains itself there will continue to be a high rate of poverty in America (say, 20 percent of the population). What I have tried to do in this chapter is to find out who is probably right. What I have concluded is that the Socialists are closer to the truth. This eliminates the last strand of plausibility in the Utopian viewpoint.

However, Socialists, if they are right on the issue of poverty, are right for the wrong reasons. Utopians presuppose a fixed absolute income approach to poverty; this I have shown to be unacceptable. Socialists usually defend their view on the basis of a variable relative income approach, but this theory also proved to be unacceptable.

The fixed absolute income approach fails because of its assumption that the costs of satisfying subsistence needs, and thus of avoiding poverty, remain fixed over time and place. It consequently underestimates the incidence of poverty for relatively advanced socioeconomic systems, and it overestimates it for relatively backward socioeconomic systems. The variable relative income approach fails because of its assumption that subsistence needs fluctuate significantly over time and place. It consequently overestimates the incidence of poverty for relatively advanced and inegalitarian socioeconomic systems, and it underestimates it for relatively backward and egalitarian socioeconomic systems.

The only approach compatible with our perceptions is the variable absolute income approach. It allows for the continued upgrading of the poverty line in societies where the real costs for appropriating the instruments necessary for the satisfaction of subsistence needs and for overcoming the obstacles to the satisfaction of these needs are continually on the increase. And it allows for the possibility of a high incidence of poverty in conjunction with much equality, and for a low incidence of poverty in conjunction with much inequality. In the abstract, the variable absolute income approach is neutral on the disagreement between Socialists and Utopians. However, in conjunction with a number of very plausible factual claims concerning trends of various sorts in advanced capitalist societies, it does support the Socialist position that the incidence of poverty is not decreasing in advanced capitalist societies. So the Socialist view seems correct, but for reasons that Socialists do not usually give. Could the variable absolute income approach to poverty be assimilated in the overall Socialist theory of society to replace the variable relative income approach? It seems to me that it could.

If the rate of poverty in America is not decreasing as technology develops, then a very important kind of scarcity is not being reduced by technological growth alone. I have argued earlier that other kinds of scarcity do not seem to be decreasing either (such as the scarcity experienced by the compulsive consumer whose wants seem always to be growing). So the Socialist critique of the Utopian view seems quite effective. If technology does not at least lead systematically to the decline of scarcity, then the Utopian view of technology loses all credibility, for the ability of technology to solve all major social problems on its own was based on its assumed ability to solve the problem of scarcity.

Notes

[1]See chapter 10.

[2]See p. 178; cf. also Donella H. Meadows, David L. Meadows, Jørgen Randers, and William H. Berens III, *The Limits of Growth* (New York: Universe Books, 1972), pp. 56–59; Harry Magdoff, *The Age of Imperialism* (New York: Monthly Review, 1969), pp. 45–54; Paul R. Ehrlich and Anne H. Ehrlich, *Population, Resources. Environment*, 2nd ed. (San Francisco: Freeman, 1972), pp. 72–73; *Scientific American* 24, (September 1971), p. 42.

[3]Cf. Robert I. Rhodes, ed., *Imperialism and Underdevelopment* (New York: Monthly Review, 1970), pp. 83–85, 90, 130; James Petras and Maurice Zeitlin, eds., *Latin America: Reform or Revolution?* (New York: Fawcett, 1968), pp. 213–215.

[4]Herman P. Miller, *Rich Man, Poor Man* (New York: Crowell, 1971), p. 41.

[5]Bradley Schiller, *The Economics of Poverty and Discrimination* (Englewood Cliffs, N.J.: Prentice-Hall, 1973). pp. 14–15; Miller, *Rich Man, Poor Man*, pp. 117–118.

[6]Miller, *Rich Man, Poor Man*, pp. 117–118.

[7]Schiller, *Economics of Poverty and Discrimination*, pp. 19–20; S. M. Miller and Pamela Roby, *The Future of Inequality* (New York: Basic Books, 1970), pp. 47–48.

[8]Karl Marx, *Capital*, Vol. I, pp. 170–171.

[9]Paul A. Baran and Paul M. Sweezy, *Monopoly Capital* (New York: Monthly Review, 1966), pp. 285–289; Ernest Mandel, *Marxist Economic Theory* (London: Merlin, 1968), pp. 150–154.

[10]Miller, *Rich Man, Poor Man*, p. 120.

[11]Miller and Roby, *Future of Inequality*, p. 42.

[12]David Mermelstein, ed., *Economics: Mainstream Readings and Radical Critiques* (New York: Random House, 1970), p. 270. Emphasis added.

[13]Miller and Roby, *Future of Inequality*, p. 36.

[14]Oscar Ornati, *Poverty Amidst Affluence* (New York: The Twentieth Century Fund, 1966), pp. 31–33.

[15]Schiller, *Economics of Poverty and Discrimination*, p. 7.

[16]Miller and Roby, *Future of Inequality*, pp. 84–142; *Report of the National Advisory Commission on Civil Disorders* (New York: Bantam, 1968), pp. 266–278; David Caplevits, *The Poor Pay More* (New York: Free Press, 1967).

[17]Philip M. Stern, *The Rape of the Taxpayer* (New York: Random House, 1973), pp. 24–25.

13

History, Dialectics, and the Prospects for Emancipation

In Search of a Socialist Theory of Technology

The last two chapters have shown that Socialists can make a powerful, and perhaps decisive, criticism of both the Utopian and Dystopian views on technology and society while admitting the good points of each. But this is not enough to ensure the success of the Socialist view. In addition to criticizing other views, Socialists must present their own positive view of technology and society, which in turn should be open to criticism. Merely showing that other views are false does not show that one's own view is true. In this chapter, I will attempt to determine the value (if any) of the positive component of the Socialist view of technology and society.

However, at this point we should be careful not to draw too hard a line between negative criticisms and positive theory. In our analysis of the Socialists' negative criticisms of other views, we have been indirectly exposed to many of the positive ingredients of the Socialist view of technology and society. Clearly, in their arguments against the Utopian and Dystopian views Socialists imply a commitment to the following substantive claims: technology is an important force in social change, but not the primary or determining force; technological growth is necessary for social progress, but does not ensure it; whether or not technology is progressive depends on which economic class controls its development and implementation; within mature capitalism, technological growth is having an increasingly deleterious and regressive impact on society; and only within socialism will the progressive potential of technology be fully realized.

As they stand, however, these claims, definitive of the Socialist view, are abstract and ambiguous, and they raise more questions than they answer. For example, if technology does not determine social change, then precisely what is its relation to social change? What generally is the place of technology within the historical process? Specifically, how does technology interact with capitalism; how has it contributed to its rise, and how will it contribute to its fall? On what basis can it be argued that technology (which is having such ill effects under industrial or postindustrial capitalism) will have overall beneficial effects under industrial or postindustrial socialism? Why should technology behave any differently under socialism than it has under capitalism?

If we turn to the Socialist literature for answers to these questions, we are bound to be disappointed. Most Socialist groups do not seem to have developed any systematic position on these questions, and we can suspect that if they had they would have been in considerable disagreement with each other. Only the Marxists have made any serious attempt to develop a coherent positive view of the social role of technology. Even here there is some disagreement, and the positions are somewhat vague and unfinished.

In the remainder of this chapter, I will limit myself to giving a brief sketch of the Marxist view of technology and society. I will base my interpretation mainly on the writings of Karl Marx (with some help from V. I. Lenin and Mao Tse-tung) since recent Marxists have not gone much beyond him on this topic. Karl Marx was one of the first modern social thinkers to take seriously the question of the impact of technology on modern society, and certainly was one of the first to give the concept of technology an important role in his overall social theory. Unfortunately, his remarks on this topic are scattered throughout his writings. There is no one work or part of a work in which the social role of technology is discussed in a systematic and detailed way. And what he says is open to a number of interpretations. As a consequence, my sketch of his view, I am afraid, will be somewhat brief and superficial. His overall theory of technology and society is not well understood (even by its supporters), and it is not sufficiently well developed.

Humans as Tool-making Animals

According to Marx, technology has always had a very important place in human life. Indeed, in Marx's scheme, one of the essential features of being human is being a tool maker; humans might even be distinguished from other animals as the tool-making animals par excellence.

Marx does not distinguish humans from animals in terms of their "souls" (of which he denies any existence), nor primarily in terms of their mental capacities. Abstract thinking and culture are late developments in the history and prehistory of humans. Humans were not always mathematical wizards, philosophers, or designers of laws and governments. But humans have always had to produce their own means of subsistence, and according to Marx it is in virtue of the way in which they produce their means of subsistence that humans mark themselves off from other animals. All other distinguishing traits of humans (both intellectual and cultural), are accounted for by the distinctive ways in which humans produce or labor. Unlike other animals, humans perform their labor with premeditation and planning, they can modify their labor extensively and improve it indefinitely, and they labor in cooperation with other humans in an endless variety of ways. Finally, in all ages, humans have labored with tools of their own making.[1]

Clearly, if as Marx believes humans are to be distinguished from other animals primarily by the way in which they produce or labor, then they are to be distinguished from other animals primarily by the fact that they make and use their own tools. In this view, humans are not only the only technological animals; that they are technological animals is one of their primary distinguishing traits, one of the primary features of their natures.

Technology and History

According to Marx, humans are by nature not only technological animals, but also historical animals. It is of their nature to have a history;

that is, to go through economic, political, and cultural transformations through time. It should be no surprise that, for Marx, technology and historical change are intertwined. Let us see what form this intertwining takes.

Marx has a dialectical view of history. That is, according to him, all or most societies go through major economic, political, and cultural transformations which occur through some revolutionary rather than evolutionary process and which are brought about primarily by internal contradictions in those societies rather than by external pressures (such as climate or war) imposed on them. The key to understanding major historical transformations lies therefore in understanding the major contradictions which arise in societies.[2]

As is well known, Marx believes that the major contradictions of society occur in the sphere of production; that is, all major contradictions occurring in the political, cultural, and intellectual spheres are in some way caused by contradictions in the productive sphere. As a consequence, all major noneconomic social transformations (such as political, cultural, and intellectual transformations) are caused by major economic transformations. The key to understanding all major social transformations lies in understanding economic transformations. For example, the rise of Protestantism and parliamentary democracy is supposed to have been caused by the transition from a feudal system of production to a capitalist system of production.[3]

How do major economic transformations come about? What sorts of contradictions in the productive sphere elicit major changes in the system of production? And what is the origin of these contradictions? These are the primary questions confronting the Marxist theory of history, and it is at this point that technology enters the stage of Marxist analysis.

Marx's account of major economic transformations goes as follows. There have been only a few major kinds of economic transformations (like the transition from slave economies to feudal economies and from feudal economies to capitalist economies) in Western Europe. These and other major transformations in economic systems have been the result of the dialectical interplay of what Marx refers to as productive forces and production relations.

Production relations are the constituents of economic systems; economic systems are defined in terms of the production relations which make them up. A production relation is any power relation between humans, or between humans and things, which they have in virtue of their roles in the production process. Within the production process, persons take on the roles of producers, overseers, controllers, and the like, and things function as raw materials, instruments of production, and so on. In virtue of these roles, persons have power over other persons or over things, or are subject to the power of other persons. These relations of power are production relations. For example, private ownership, as a relation of production, is a power relation between persons (the controllers of production) and things (say, the instruments of production); the act of hiring institutes power relations of relevance to production between persons (such as between capitalists and wage laborers).

Different economic systems are made up of somewhat different and somewhat overlapping production relationships. Private ownership of the means of production is a production relationship common both to feudalism and capitalism. But there are differences in the production relations of each of these systems. For example, the producers (workers) within capitalism can sell their labor to whichever capitalist they please; the producers within feudalism (serfs) are bound to their lord for life. In each of these systems the producers have different production relationships with the owners of the means of production for whom they produce.[4]

Productive forces are those elements involved in production contributing to the productivity of workers (such as skills, tools, machinery, raw materials, and organization of the work force). The productive forces of a society can roughly be identified with the technology of that society. (Only "roughly" because some productive forces, such as raw materials, are not technologies or embodiments thereof.) Growth of the productive forces can roughly be equated with growth in technology.[5]

In talking about the interaction of productive forces and production relationships, Marx in effect is talking about the interaction of technologies and production relationships. How does this interaction contribute to major economic transformations?

Productive forces do not grow all by themselves. They grow because there is an economic incentive for them to grow. They may grow as a consequence of the need to survive (for example, the development of irrigation techniques in arid climates) or simply as a consequence of the drive for profits (as is the case with the railroads). This is to say that the productive forces (technology) only grow when stimulated by the production relationships (the economic system). The productive forces may stagnate for centuries because there is no incentive in the system of production relationships for them to develop. Consider the many centuries, and even millenia, through which the technology of hunting and gathering societies has survived in an almost unchanged form. Actually, it is only with the advent of capitalism that sustained and almost automatic development of the productive forces has been generated by the system of production relationships. Other systems of production relationships have only generated technological change over relatively short periods of time. For example, the great development of agriculture (in which occurred the invention of the horse collar and the heavy plow), spurred on by the feudal economic system during the tenth and eleventh centuries, was followed by four centuries of stagnation in agricultural technology.[6]

Major economic revolutions are precipitated when productive forces and production relations come into conflict. This happens when a set of production relationships stimulates the introduction of new productive forces whose existence is incompatible with the existence of these production relationships. It is as if the production relationships create the very conditions of their own destruction (in this case new productive forces). In any conflict of productive forces and production relationships, the productive forces win. When in conflict with the prevailing production relationships, the productive forces stimulate the destruction of these production relationships and call into being a new set of production relationships compatible with them. Feudalism was destroyed because it called into existence certain contradictory productive forces which were more compatible with capitalism than with it. Capitalism will similarly break down and be replaced by socialism because it has generated new productive forces incompatible with it but compatible with socialism.[7]

Consider the following examples given by Marx. The growth of the medieval towns within the heart of the feudal agrarian system made possible the development of manufacturing skills which could best be exploited in factories rather than in home industries. But the development of factories brought the feudal system crashing down and facilitated the rise of the bourgeoisie.[8]

Or consider the case of capitalism, another system of production relations. Capitalism made unprecedented contributions to the growth of the productive forces. It ushered humankind into the industrial age in technology:

> The bourgeoisie, during its rule of scarce one hundred years, has created more massive and more colossal productive forces than all the preceding generations together. Subjection of Nature's forces to man, machinery, application of chemistry to industry and agriculture, steam-navigation, railways, electric telegraphs, clearing of whole continents for cultivation, canalization of rivers, whole populations conjured out of the ground— what earlier century had even a presentiment that such productive forces slumbered in the lap of social labor.[9]

And it unleashed a period of sustained technological growth which has yet to come to a close.

> The bourgeoisie cannot exist without constantly revolutionizing the instruments of production, and thereby the relations of production, and with them the whole relations of society. Conservation of the old modes of production in unaltered form, was, on the contrary, the first condition of existence for all earlier industrial classes. Constant revolutionizing of production, uninterrupted disturbance of all social conditions, everlasting uncertainty and agitation distinguish the bourgeois epoch from all the earlier ones.[10]

But the technological growth which capitalism has stimulated is now coming back to haunt it. Capitalism is losing control over its own productive forces.

> Modern bourgeois society, with its relations of production, of exchange, and of property, a society that has conjured up such gigantic means of production and of exchange, is like the sorcerer, who is no longer able to control the power of the nether world whom he has called up by his . spells.[11]

The development of industrial technology (the new productive forces) supposedly will bring about the breakdown of capitalism (a system of production relations) and its replacement by socialism (another system of production relations). For capitalism, it is claimed, will be rent asunder by class conflicts and economic crises made inevitable by the maturation of industrial technology. Industrial technology under capitalism has brought large masses of workers together in the same workplaces and has substantially increased their literacy, but at the same time has intensified their sense of alienation and deprivation. This last factor, according to Marx, could only lead to increased class consciousness, militancy, and organized power on the part of the workers. Furthermore, the growth of the industrial productive forces, according to Marx, could only sharpen the economic crises within capitalism. For example, capitalism spurs consistent growth in productivity, but growth in productivity leads to crises of underconsumption (and with it unemployment). Marx also gives technical arguments to prove that the massive introduction of machinery by capitalism into the production process will ultimately lead to a decreasing rate of profit, and a consequent intensifying crisis. Marx believed that out of the deepening crises and increasing worker insurrection should come the demise of capitalism and the birth of socialism.[12]

In conclusion, let us say that, according to Marx, all major economic transformations and hence all major social transformations are the result of the dialectical interaction of productive forces (technology) and production relations. Productive forces grow only when stimulated by production relations. At some time, the production relations of a society generate a set of productive forces which come in conflict with them. These production relations then give way to the productive forces and are supplanted by a new system of production relations more compatible with the productive forces. This, in essence, is an economic revolution.

Technology obviously (according to Marx) plays an important role in social change. But for him it is neither the only nor the primary determinant of social change. Along with the set of production relations, it is one of the two primary determinants of social change. Growth in technology (growth in the productive forces) is determined by the production relations; production relations are in turn transformed by growth in technology.

Technology and Progress

It is an oversimplification to say, as I have said earlier, that technology is for Marx socially progressive in socialist economies, and socially regressive in economies whose means of production are privately owned (as in feudalism and capitalism). The picture is somewhat more complicated than that. Marx looks upon technology as a genuinely progressive force throughout the whole of history, even in class societies (societies in which a small minority is the ruling class). Technology for Marx is not only an important source of social change, but also an important measure of social progress. Of course, Marx does not deemphasize the evil effects that technology has had throughout human history. The emergence of agrarian technology, for example, made possible the rise of ruling minority classes, tyranny, exploitation, inequality, and warfare. (Primitive hunting and gathering societies, as already indicated, had no ruling classes, little economic inequality, mostly commonly owned property, and considerably less warfare.) Marx has described in detail all the evil effects of industrial technology within capitalism. But despite all its undesirable consequences, Marx still thinks that technological growth (the growth of the productive forces) has contributed overall more good than evil through history (though the amount of good may not be much greater than the amount of evil). For one thing, technological growth (in Marx's view) is good in itself, since it is the expression of one of the highest creative powers of humankind. Second, it has contributed much to wealth and leisure, however unfairly these may have been distributed. Third, it has made possible the gifts of civilization, such as the arts and sciences. Marx is not a primitivist; he is fully committed to the advancement of civilization. Finally, technological growth has paved the way for socialism and communism, which could not exist in the absence of very advanced productive capacities.[13]

In many ways, Marx seems closer to the Utopians than the Dystopians. Still, there remain basic irreconcilable differences between Marx's and the Utopians' positions on technology and progress. First, for Marx, technology is not the only determinant of social change, and hence not the only cause of social progress (the production relations having an equally important role). Second, Marx attributes more evil consequences to the use of technology than the Utopians do. Third, technology is not for Marx ultimately responsible for all the good that it has been used to bring about. Fourth, Marx greatly qualifies his claims about the progressiveness of technology in societies ruled by minority classes (such as feudalism and capitalism). Though he admits that overall technology is progressive in the early and developing stages of each class society, he emphasized that overall it becomes destructive in the twilight stages of each class society. Finally, Marx denies that scientists and technicians, or technology taken abstractly, rather than manual workers, are the contemporary agents of human emancipation. All these considerations serve to keep Marx far away from the Utopian camp, no matter how closely he may seem to veer toward it.

Technology under Socialism and Communism

Marxists, unlike other Socialists, postulate two stages in the development of worker-controlled economies after the demise of capitalism. Capitalism, according to them, will be followed by socialism, and socialism by communism. Socialism, in this view, is merely a transitional stage between capitalism and communism.

In both socialism and communism, workers democratically control the production processes. Where such is not the case, neither socialism nor communism exists in the Marxian sense. But socialism and communism differ in important respects.

First, communism is a classless society; it has only one economic class—the working class. Other classes persist in socialism, such as the bourgeoisie and the peasantry. As socialism gradually develops the members of the bourgeoisie and peasantry are transformed into members of the working class. (For the peasantry this begins to happen when agricultural production is collectivized.)

Second, communism is a postscarcity society, a society of abundance, whereas socialism still exists in scarcity.

Third, communism only comes into being once the political state "withers away." Communism is a stateless society, that is, a society without institutions for imposing force or inflicting legal violence (through the use of police and jails). Some sort of political state continues to exist under socialism; under it, the working class needs political force to suppress counterrevolutionary groups and to impose some discipline on a restructured and still insufficiently productive economy. The absence of contending classes under communism, as well as of economic scarcity, does away with the foregoing reasons for the use of political force. As socialism develops and approaches communism

> People will gradually become accustomed to observing the elementary rules of social life that have been known for centuries and repeated for thousands of years in all copy-book maxims; they will become accustomed to observing them without force, without compulsion, without subordination, without the special apparatus of compulsion which is called the state.[14]

Fourth, in communism the distinction between physical and mental work has been eliminated. Automation will make possible full participation by workers in planning, management, and research, and it will require little or no physical work.

Finally, in communism goods are so abundant and tasks so minimal that they can be distributed according to the principle, "from each according to his capacities, and to each according to his needs." That is, under communism, there is no correlation between how much one gets and how much (or how well) one works. However, in socialism, one's income is proportionate to one's work.[15]

It should be clear that in a real communist society technology would have both a very important and a highly beneficial role. To see this does not require any great insight. Communism is by definition an ideal or utopian society; people get all they need without coercion and burdensome work. These conditions being met, it is difficult to see how anything could go wrong socially, or how it could be caused by technology. Where postscarcity exists, there can be no technologically induced ecological crisis. Where the working class is in control and there are no other classes there can be no technocratic tyranny, no mass manipulation, no oppression, and no unfreedom; there cannot be any Brave New World. Where producers control their own work and where the distinction between mental and physical work is eradicated there can be no alienation from work. Where leisure and abundance prevail the conditions for sexual repression disappear.

Indeed, the good things about communism are in part (and only in part) due to modern technology. Abundance, leisure, the elimination of the distinction between mental and physical work, the use of non-coercive means of nurturing and training—all of these presuppose a highly developed state of technology.

The real question is not whether technology would function beneficially within communism, but whether real communism will come to pass after all. Marx can be criticized, not for opting for something bad (clearly communism is not that), but for opting for something unreal. What reasons do Marx and his followers have for believing that socialism will lead to communism? The arguments usually presented are sketchy, but this is not due to neglect. Marx himself never wanted to engage in empty speculation. He actually said very little about communism. He only wanted to speak about what could be proven scientifically. He focused more on the present than on the future; he concentrated on trying to determine the laws of capitalism. However, if he could come to understand the contradictions of capitalism, he could begin to make predictions on the way in which capitalism would end. From this, he could also make predictions about what sort of system would follow capitalism. But these projections into the future could only be vague, and the farther into the future they were made, the vaguer and more useless they would become. For this reason, he found it difficult to speak confidently about the nature of communism or about the causes within socialism which would lead to it.[16]

But what of socialism? What kind of role would technology have within precommunist socialism? Here again the presumption would be in favor of an overall beneficial role, though in this case the presumption would not be quite so strong. If workers control society (as they would under real socialism), they will attempt to minimize alienation from their work, environmental pollution, and resource depletion. They will attempt to put some restraints on the discretionary power of their elected managers and technicians. But this may not come so easily, for socialist societies exist in economic scarcity. The struggle against economic scarcity is one of the first orders of business for socialist societies. But success in this struggle may require some painful decisions; it may require allowing a little more pollution, alienation, and bureaucracy than the workers would otherwise have wanted. Indeed, too many concessions of this sort could subvert socialist society and transform it into something quite different.

This problem is especially acute when socialist revolutions take place in economically backward societies (such as Russia and China). Here the struggle against scarcity may be so intense and desperate that it may elicit concessions from the working class which are inconsistent with the development of socialist society. Mao Tse-tung has repeatedly pointed to the dangers of unfettered technological growth in backward socialist societies. He has warned against the temptation to place technological growth above everything else. Such behavior, he claims, can only lead to the sort of technologically induced evils that capitalism is famous for.

This issue came to a head in the Cultural Revolution in China. The forces of Mao Tse-tung, emphasizing close political control over technology and its growth (the policy of "politics takes command"), confronted the forces of Liu Shao-ch'i emphasizing a wholly enthusiastic commitment to maximal technological and economic growth, efficiency, and productive rationality (the policy of "technics takes command"). Liu Shao-ch'i thought that the development of socialism would take care of itself once the forces of technology and modern production were unleashed. He seemed to favor any kind of incentive system (such as high salaries for technocrats) which would speed up China's movement toward modernization.

Mao attacked Liu for "taking the capitalist road." He was convinced that Liu's policy of "technics takes command" would have the effect of reintroducing capitalist social relations under the socialist umbrella. For example, the policy of giving technological growth top priority would inevitably give rise to a privileged class of technocrats and bureaucrats, separated from the people and more interested in careerism and personal aggrandizement than in the imperatives of socialism. These technocrats and bureaucrats would mimic their capitalist counterparts. They would compulsively push for growth and accumulation above all else; they would set up authoritarian lines of decision making throughout the economy; they would exacerbate the distinction between physical and mental labor; they would transform most physical work (in the name of efficiency) into unskilled and monotonous activity; they would tend to decentralize all decision making; they would encourage individualism, competition, and the struggle for monetary reward; they would proliferate bureaucratic red tape; they would increase the dependence of technologically backward China on the technologically more advanced Soviet Union and United States. Though these technocrats and bureaucrats would not actually be capitalists, they would behave very much like the technocrats and bureaucrats working under the sway of capitalism.

During the Cultural Revolution, the Maoists instituted a number of reforms to correct the excesses of the policy of "technics takes command," as well as to prevent such a policy from taking effect in the future. One of the most dramatic ploys was the institutionalization of "three-in-one" committees. Every factory, and indeed every decision-making subcomponent of every factory, was to be run by a three-in-one committee of revolutionary cadres, workers, and technicians. Technicians were never to be left alone; they were to interact with workers and party members at every level of decision making. And technicians could not appeal to their expertise in order to intimidate workers and cadres during the decision making process. A number of educational programs were instituted to provide cadres and workers with some of this expertise; such educated workers and cadres would then take part in research projects with technicians and scientists. Meanwhile, technicians would be periodically sent out to work in the countryside or in the production lines of factories. On the other side, production workers would rotate jobs among each other to decrease alienation, to acquire more skill, and to broaden their grasp of the factory as an integrated system. The Maoists fought for increasing decentralization of production, thus undercutting the apparent indispensability and the power base of bureaucrats and technocrats. Finally, they encouraged each productive enterprise to be as self-sufficient as possible, thus again reducing their dependence on planners from afar; plants engaged in the manufacture of final products would thus make their own machine tools, lathes, and the like. Such success would inevitably increase the self-confidence of local workers and lessen their tendency to always look to outside experts for help and advice.[17]

In conclusion, it could be argued persuasively that in real socialism (that is, socialism in which there is workers' control) technology would tend to be used beneficially rather than harmfully. However, the dangers of harmful use would still be there (not as in communism), and they would be greater as the backwardness of the socialist society in question was greater.

As in communism, however, the most pressing question is not whether technology will be used beneficially within real socialism, but whether there is any reliable trend toward real socialism. Is history moving toward real socialism, or is real socialism merely a pipe dream? Again, what basis did Marx and his followers have for believing that the demise of capitalism (supposing that this indeed takes place) will be followed by the emergence of worker-controlled societies? Many theorists are very cynical about the possibility of a worker-controlled economy. They think that any attempt to institute a democratically controlled economy is doomed to failure; the electoral process will gradually be subverted and a small elite (whether or not elected) will in effect take over the economy and run it to suit its own purposes. Majority rule will deteriorate quickly into minority rule.

Regrettably, recent history seems to support the view of the cynics. Practically every socialist revolution in this century has culminated in tyranny by the few. The working class has found itself neither more free nor less oppressed after these socialist revolutions than it had been before under capitalism. There is no real socialism (worker control) in the Soviet Union, in Eastern Europe, or in North Korea. The state, which controls the economy in the Soviet Union, is in turn controlled by a small clique. There is no doubt that the Soviet masses are subject to the dictates of a minority ruling class; the only controversy concerns the nature of this ruling class. Is it a reconstituted capitalist class, as some Maoists have suggested, or is it a bureaucratic class? Is the Soviet Union a state capitalist society, or is it a bureaucratic centralist society? The only sure thing is that it is not socialist.

Being an elitist state, the Soviet Union, not surprisingly, has used technology just as harmfully as the capitalist societies of the West. Pollution abounds, work alienation is widespread, and mass manipulation is the order of the day. And what is true of the Soviet Union is true of all Eastern European countries that claim to be socialist.

China seems somewhat of an exception, but only somewhat. The government has a broader popular base and makes decisions with greater sensitivity and greater concern for human welfare. It has made significant strides in humanizing the impact of productive technology on the home and work environments. Nonetheless, China is not strictly speaking a socialist society. Its affairs are clearly still run by a bureaucratic elite, albeit a relatively benevolent one; in China, the producers do not control the economy and the state. Meanwhile, the leadership seems to be turning its back on the gains of the Cultural Revolution. China is still a long way off from the ideal of Marxist socialism.

Are we to agree with the cynics that real socialism is impossible because real democracy is impossible? We should be careful here not to take too rigid a view of human history. All the evidence is not in yet. And there have been periods in human history (such as when hunting and gathering societies prevailed) when real democracy was possible and even actualized. Furthermore, real socialism seems to provide the only hope now for a technologically sane future. All the societies controlled by a small minority (such as the United States and Russia) continue to use technology in a desperate and disastrous way; they are speeding us toward catastrophe. Real socialism may well be the only alternative to this technologically induced catastrophe. Real socialism may well provide us with the only opportunity for both releasing the emancipatory and for containing the destructive powers of modern technology. If this is so, then the cynic's attitude, through perhaps difficult to now refute, is in practice self-defeating.

Conclusion

The Socialists' positive views of technology and society are not as well developed as their negative criticisms of other views. Indeed, only the Marxists among Socialists have developed a systematic theory of the interconnections between technology and society. I reconstructed the main lines of Marx's view in this chapter, beginning with his broad claims about the interrelation between technology and history and between technology and progress, ending with his more specific claims about the role of technology within capitalism and socialism. His view, though interesting, seems too vague; too many questions are left unanswered and too many issues unresolved. And much of the confirmatory or disconfirmatory evidence for Marx's view is still too far in the future.

Notes

[1]Karl Marx and Friedrich Engels, *German Ideology* (New York: International Publishers, 1947), pp. 1–43.

[2]Ibid., Karl Marx, "Preface" to *A Contribution to the Critique of Political Economy*, in Karl Marx and Friedrich Engels, *Selected Works* (New York: International, 1968), pp. 181–185; Friedrich Engels, "Socialism: Utopian or Scientific," in *Selected Works*, pp. 399–434.

[3]Marx, "Preface."

[4]Marx, "Preface"; Karl Marx and Friedrich Engels, "Communist Manifesto," in *Selected Works*, pp. 35–63.

[5]Karl Marx, *Capital*, Vol. I (New York: International, 1967), pp. 40, 314.

[6]Ibid., pp. 485–486; Marx and Engels, *Selected Works*, p. 38.

[7]Cf. Marx, "Preface," "Communist Manifesto," and Engels, "Socialism: Utopian or Scientific," all in Marx and Engels, *Selected Works*.

[8]Ibid., as well as Marx and Engels, *German Ideology*, pp. 43–63.

[9]Marx and Engels, *Selected Works*, pp. 39–40.

[10]Ibid., p. 38.

[11]Ibid., p. 40.

[12]Cf. Engels, "Socialism: Utopian or Scientific"; Marx and Engels, "The Communist Manifesto"; Marx, *Capital*, Vol. I, pp. 761–764; Karl Marx, *Capital*, Vol. III (New York: International Publishers, 1967), p. 211–266.

[13]See, for example, Karl Marx, *Grundrisse* (New York: Random House, 1973), p. 158, 162, 305–308; Marx, *Capital*, Vol. III, p. 819.

[14]V. I. Lenin, "State and Revolution," in *Essential Works of Lenin* (New York: Bantam, 1966), p. 338.

[15]Marx, "Critique of the Gotha Program," in Marx and Engels, *Selected Works*, pp. 315–335; Lenin, "State and Revolution," pp. 333–349.

[16]Lenin, "State and Revolution," p. 334.

[17]Cf. Mao Tse-tung, "On the Correct Handling of Contradictions Among the People," in *Four Essays on Philosophy* (Peking: For. Lang. Press,1968), pp. 79–113; Committee of Concerned Asian Scholars, *China: Inside the People's Republic* (New York: Bantam, 1972); Staff of *Science for the People*, *China: Science Walks on Two Legs* (New York: Avon, 1974); E. L. Wheelwright and Bruce McFarlane, *The Chinese Road to Socialism* (New York: Monthly Review, 1970); William Hinton, *Turning Point in China* (New York: Monthly Review, 1972).

14

___

Conclusion

The Two Major Questions

My analysis of the Utopian, Dystopian, and Socialist views is complete. It is now time to take stock. In this chapter I will summarize what I have tried to accomplish, and point out the key issues still in need of resolution.

Of the questions dealing with the social role of technology, I have focused on two which are especially pressing and important. The first concerns the extent and nature of the impact of technology on social institutions and individual lives. The second involves the extent to which this impact is socially beneficial, and the extent to which it is socially harmful. These are questions which weigh on us considerably as we reflect on the potential crises and calamities of the next fifty years. Technology is strongly intertwined with our future prospects. We are deeply worried about the power technology may have over us, and the suffering and dislocation it may visit on us.

My purpose has been to clarify these and other related questions and to critically analyze the answers usually given them. This has not been a straightforward task. There is no general consensus, nor even a consensus within the various schools, on exactly how to respond to these questions; the responses provided are, for the most part, vague and incomplete. I have distinguished among three vastly different views which systematically seek to answer these questions—the Utopian, Dystopian, and Socialist views. There are views other than these, but they are so inchoate and confused that nothing much can be done with them.

The problem has been to determine which of these views gives the best answer, and whether the best answer is good enough. After much analysis and debate, both the Utopian and Dystopian views were shown to be grossly inadequate, and most probably false. The Socialist view was not shown to be false, but neither was it shown to be fully adequate. The Socialist view, however, did provide arguments to refute the other two views. In this respect, some parts of the Socialist view were shown to be true. These are primarily its negative claims; its positive claims remain unproven.

From a critical study of the Utopian, Dystopian, and Socialist views, we were able to provide only a partial and negative answer to the most pressing questions about the social role of technology. The answer goes as follows: Technology is not the only or primary cause of major social change; technology is not, of itself, primarily responsible for the benefits it bestows or the harms it inflicts on society; whether or not technology is socially beneficial or harmful depends ultimately on which social classes control it; capitalist and so-called "socialist" societies are presently using technology in increasingly harmful ways, and in potentially catastrophic ways; these societies seem incapable of releasing the liberating powers of technology. (The one possible exception is the People's Republic of China.)

Many issues, unfortunately, remain unresolved. For example, we have not been able to determine the precise nature of the interaction between technological change and social change. Nor have we gathered sufficient evidence for us to believe with any confidence that technologically harmful systems, like capitalism and so-called "socialism," can and will be supplanted by some social system (such as "real" socialism) which maximizes the benefits of technology while minimizing its drawbadks.

The Utopian View

It would be grossly misleading, and somewhat unfair, to summarize what we have learned about and from each of these three global views by exclusively appealing to labels like "is false," "is true," "has been disproven," and "has been partially proven." It would be especially wrong to dismiss the Utopian and Dystopian views out of hand for being unqualifiedly (and perhaps obviously) false. Though indeed false, the Utopian and Dystopian views nonetheless incorporate many insights which too many of us are prone to disregard or forget. And where these views fail, they fail in an interesting and challenging manner, and finding out why they fail where they do teaches us much about the truth of these matters. It has been as important for me to show that the Utopian and Dystopian views must be taken seriously and studied carefully as it has been to show that they are false. And though I side ultimately with the Socialists, I think the latter have much to learn from these two opposing views.

The Utopian view has been especially subject to undeserved abuse and ridicule. It must be admitted that, at least in the 1970s, its predictions seem wholly unsubstantiated by the facts. Economic scarcity and human aggression do not seem to be declining as technology is growing. Human misery, if anything, seems on the upswing, and things seem to be "running out of control."

Paradoxically, despite the wholesale failure of its predictions, the Utopian view still has considerable appeal, and the argument usually given in defense of it seems quite persuasive and challenging. This is due to the fact that the Utopian argument proceeds from assumptions which are widely accepted today. For example, it is almost universally believed that technology will continue to grow indefinitely. I suspect that a majority of those who have seriously reflected on these matters believe that we are undergoing a major technological revolution, that managers and technicians control the corporate system, that scientific knowledge is the highest form of human knowledge, that economic problems are strategically the most important social problems, that humans have the potential to solve their own social problems, and that human behavior can be modified dramatically through environmental and genetic manipulation. Furthermore, a significant number believe that technology is the primary cause of major social change, that technology can solve the problems which it creates, that poverty can be eliminated, and that society should be ruled by experts (and only by experts). But note that the above beliefs, when conjoined, inevitably lead one to the Utopian conclusion. The Utopian conclusion is not based on bizarre, far-out, or abnormal assumptions; it is strongly rooted in conventional beliefs and popular biases. If indeed the Utopian view is naive and silly, then some of the more entrenched popular beliefs are also naive and silly. Many social theorists, I suspect, who dismiss the Utopian view as wholly implausible may actually be unknowingly committed by their systems of beliefs to this view. In discussing the Utopian view, an important part of my objective has been to show that one cannot reject the Utopian view without rejecting some highly popular theories held within various social science disciplines.

Each major assumption underlying the Utopian view is shared by either the Dystopian or the Socialist view. The Utopian view thus provides a framework for defining each of these other views. For example, Dystopians accept the Utopian assumptions that technology determines social change and that modern societies are being transformed into technocracies. Socialists accept the Utopian assumptions that economic problems are the primary social problems and that human behavior can be radically transformed for the better through modifications in the natural and social environments. But note the implication of this. Since the Utopian view is false, then at least one of its supporting assumptions is false. But this false assumption—whatever it is—is also shared by either the Dystopian or Socialist view. Consequently, this assumption, in virtue of its falsity, destroys not only the Utopian view but either the Dystopian or the Socialist view as well. I have shown that it is the Dystopian view that suffers more from the assumptions it shares with the Utopian view. The Dystopian view has to be rejected for some of the same reasons that the Utopian view has to be rejected. For example, the Dystopian view was shown to be false in part because it espouses, in agreement with the Utopian view, the false claim that technology is the major determinant of social change.

In summary, the Utopian view is deeply rooted in some of the most pervasive beliefs of our day, and it is intertwined with the other global views concerning the social role of technology. If the Utopian view is rejected, as it must be, then many of these pervasive beliefs must be rejected along with it.

The Dystopian View

The Dystopian view has an opposite appeal from the Utopian view. The Utopian view provides a strong analysis of its assumptions and a persuasive argument for its conclusion, but fails miserably in its predictions. The Dystopian view, so far, is quite successful in its predictions, but the analyses and arguments it gives in defense of its conclusion are too sketchy and unconvincing.

The power of the Dystopian view comes mainly from its ability to accurately predict the increasingly dysfunctional consequences of the uses of modern technology (such as centralized control, alienated work, and ecological breakdown). Dystopians have been warning us of this for nearly a century, but it is only recently that we have begun to seriously take note.

Dystopians especially have been articulate in dramatizing some of the serious obstacles to the resolution of social problems through modern technology. First, they have alerted us to the constraints which particular technologies impose on the choice of solutions. (For example, given certain productive technologies, such as the assembly line, there are very few options available for dealing with the problem of alienated labor.) Second, they have reminded us of the persistent failure of humans to comprehend and cope with the complicated problems of society. Third, they have forcefully driven home the paradoxes of economic growth. (For example the more economies grow, the more they need to continue to grow because of increasing artificial scarcity, such as compulsive consumerism and pollution). Finally, they have made us glaringly aware of the limits of nature; we cannot extract at will all we want from nature without destroying nature itself.

The Dystopian view then is quite successful in pointing out the evil consequences of contemporary uses of technology, and in exposing some of the obstacles to the resolution of social problems through technology. Nonetheless, the Dystopian view has to be rejected because it fails to make a good case for its central claim that technology, and not the users of technology, is ultimately at fault for the evil consequences of its uses. This failure is based on some serious misconceptions of technology and its growth. First, Dystopians do not recognize that often there are alternative technologies for achieving the same end. If among the alternative technologies (say, the technologies of automobile production) the one with the worst social effect is chosen (in this case, assembly line production), then the choosers rather than the technology chosen seem ultimately to blame for the resulting evils (here, alienated work). Second, Dystopians have grossly exaggerated the requirements of technological growth. They think, for example, that technological growth will always require growth in the gross national product (GNP). In virtue of this, they conclude that technological growth requires growth in pollution, resource depletion, and defense spending. But this conclusion is not warranted; it is false that technological growth always requires growth in the GNP.

The Socialist View

Of the three global views, the Socialist view is clearly the most sophisticated and the best worked out. Socialists have presented what I think is the most developed and successful analysis and criticism of advanced Western societies. They have shown these to be capitalist societies controlled by the capitalist class and to be incapable of resolving the basic economic problems of humankind (some of which they have themselves created or intensified).

The Socialists' most important insight is that much of what goes on in society (though not all) is determined by its economic class structure. Specifically, the economic class structure is the factor most influential in determining how technology is used, and particularly whether it is used for good or evil. Technology will continue to be used badly as long as it is controlled by minority economic classes. Utopians and Dystopians almost completely disregard this important social role of economic classes. This gives their views an air of unreality, and it ensures their falsity.

Nonetheless, the Socialist view is hampered by some important, though probably surmountable, weaknesses. First, Socialists have not paid sufficient theoretical attention to technology and the way it acts upon society. Even if technology is controlled by humans, it nonetheless imposes constraints on how it is to be controlled. (One simply cannot do what one wants with a particular technology.) Furthermore, it even has some influence in determining which class will control it. (Socialists do concede this.) Socialists have not succeeded in specifying the constraints and influences which technology reimposes on society.

Second, Socialists have not adequately defended their claim that socialism, unlike capitalism, will make use of technology in a basically humane and emancipatory way. Here they are in a double bind. If they concede that today's so-called "socialist" societies (such as the Soviet Union) are really socialist, then they will have difficulty showing that socialism makes use of technology in a more humane and emancipatory way than capitalism. If, on the other hand, they deny that these societies are really socialist, then they will be saddled with the burden of showing that real socialism, though it has not yet appeared, is historically viable and will emerge with the demise of advanced capitalism.

Third, Socialists have not sufficiently come to terms with the problems arising out of the limits of nature. They have not sufficiently taken seriously the long-run threats of virtually complete resource depletion and unavoidable pollution growth, and they have hardly inquired into the issue of curtailing economic growth. Socialists are too sanguine about the possibility that the struggle against scarcity can gradually be won without creating ecological havoc and destroying nature in the process.

Despite these difficulties, Socialism has not yet been refuted, and it remains the most promising of the global views on technology and society. Socialists must concede, however, that their view is not wholly justified by science, though it has some scientific basis. Their view is based in part on intuition, hunch, faith, and hope. But this should not be an embarrassment, for no vision of the future can at this time be fully justified by science. Intuitions, hunches, and the like are not unreliable springs for human action.

Further Questions

The controversy between optimist and pessimist views of the world's future continues unabated and without resolution. I have argued against one optimist view (the Utopian view), one pessimist view (the Dystopian view), and have partly defended a second optimist view (the Socialist view). But the optimists have not yet won the day. There are alternative pessimist views to the now-discarded Dystopian view. Consider the view which blames catastrophes predicted for the future not on technology but on the economic class structure of society. (See, for example, Robert Heilbroner's *Inquiry into the Human Prospect.*) [1]

There are some very important questions which I have not been able to resolve (although I have dealt with them), but which must be resolved before anyone can be fully justified in taking either an optimist or a pessimist stance toward the world's future. These questions are: Can scarcity be eliminated or significantly attenuated? Can the human propensity toward violence and other forms of aggression be eliminated or significantly attenuated? Can inequality in political and economic power be eliminated or significantly attenuated? If the answer to each of these questions is affirmative, then the most unabashed optimism is justified. If it is negative, then the darkest pessimism is justified. But the knowledge required to answer adequately these questions seems considerably beyond our capacity at this point. Consider each of them singly.

SCARCITY

This elusive problem continues to defy understanding and resolution. Whether the struggle against scarcity can be won depends on many factors, but especially on the fecundity of nature, the dynamics of human wants, and the organizational capacities of society.

When considering the fecundity of nature, it is important to remember that although the universe provides us with an infinite amount of potential resources, as the extraction of resources increases, so does the social cost of this extraction. The universe is not only a source of goods for humans, but also a sink for human refuse. As resource extraction increases, so does the excretion of human pollutants. There will come a time when the gains from resource extraction will be outweighed by the social costs of pollution excretion. At that point, growth in resource extraction must stop. The only question is when and at what stage of economic development this will have to happen. Some pessimists (such as Meadows, et al. in *The Limits of Growth*) say that growth will have to stop when worldwide per capita production is still quite low. According to them, we must be resigned forever to extensive poverty and deprivation. There is no way of telling now if they are right. It may well be that growth in resource extraction will not need to be curtailed until affluence is possible for everyone in the world.

To turn to the question of the dynamics of human wants, some think that human wants are infinite; that is, that no matter how much humans have, they want more. Obviously, if this is so, the elimination of scarcity is impossible; but it is not clearly so. Studies of hunting and gathering tribes have revealed peoples who seem quite satisfied with what they have. There have also been long periods in human history when wants have not grown. The phenomenon of constantly growing wants is peculiar to societies exhibiting economic growth. And now we are caught in a vicious spiral in which economic growth leads to growth in wants, and growth in wants necessitates more economic growth. This vicious spiral has to be broken, but it is not clear how it can be done.

Regarding the organizational capacities of society, the maximization of returns from nature, as well as the moderation of human wants, will require considerably more sophisticated and sensitive forms of human organization than we have now. We are rapidly learning that managing a modern economy is a difficult and frustrating task. None of the planned economies, either in the capitalist or socialist worlds, seem able to avoid crises, foul-ups, and irrational allocations and distributions. Perhaps the recent application of new intellectual technologies (such as input-output analysis and systems design), as well as of computers, will begin to alleviate these problems. And a trend toward decentralization (again made possible by the application of computers) may reduce further the bureaucratic load on economic planning.

HUMAN VIOLENCE AND OTHER FORMS OF AGGRESSION

Unfortunately, we may never see an end to the controversy between innatist and environmentalist theories of human violence and aggression. The reasons for this are many. For one thing, each kind of human drive manifests itself in a variety of behaviors; and drives can be quite severely repressed. The presence or absence of a particular drive is therefore very difficult to locate. Each human is an unbelievably complicated organism, intractable to complete scientific understanding. Humans differ greatly among each other. They live in an endless variety of environments and they are subtly influenced by the differences in these environments. A large number of potential human environments have not yet evolved historically or have not yet been fully designed. It is difficult to discern the impact of existing environments on human behavior, and prohibitively dangerous to bring about significant experimental modifications in these environments. Human groups, as well as human individuals, consistently frustrate attempts at scientific prediction. For all these reasons, it is almost impossible to determine at this time whether the dark aspects of human behavior (such as violence, cruelty, oppression, and self-destruction) spring out of and are coeval with human nature, or whether they result from historical fluctuations in the human environment. And we cannot predict with any confidence that in the more benign postscarcity environment of future societies humans will become more like angels and less like beasts.

DEMOCRACY

There is a widespread feeling that dysfunctions will continue to beset society as long as economic and political power are concentrated in the hands of a few; that is, as long as members of society cannot participate in economic and political decision making on equal terms. But real democracies have not existed since the days of hunting and gathering societies. Why should we expect that the future will give rise to them? Isn't that just another illusion? Aren't political and economic elitism just other permanent dark sides of the human historical condition? Here again it is difficult to tell. Elitism has thrived on the srruggle for scarce goods, on the reinforcement of aggressive and competitive drives, on the necessity for centralized decision making, and on the division between mental and physical labor. If decentralized, computer-assisted economic decision making is the trend of the future, if automation undermines the distinction between mental and physical work, and if the struggle for scarce goods comes to an end and human aggression can be eradicated, then elitism will not seem quite so necessary and democracy quite so illusory. At such a time, democracy may be the most natural and least dysfunctional way of organizing society.

We have a right to be skeptical that science can provide us with an answer to each of the above questions before the issue is resolved by history. Part of our crisis today springs from the inability of science to deliver to us the sort of knowledge about human society it has promised. In the absence of such knowledge, we will most probably be unable to seize our historical destiny and to direct it in accordance with our purposes. We will have to do what previous human societies have had to do, and that is muddle along with fragmented bits of information. This does not entail catastrophe, of course. Humans in the past have survived by muddling along. And perhaps we will increase our chances to ward off catastrophe by becoming less gullible about the claims of science to be able to direct our major social prognostications and decisions. Nonetheless, we should use critically whatever knowledge is available. It is my hope that what I have written here makes some contribution, however modest, to the growth of such knowledge.

Notes

[1] Robert Heilbroner, *An Inquiry into the Human Prospect* (New York: Norton, 1974).

INDEX